# Student Activities in

**ALGEBRA 1 for Christian Schools®**

**Ron Tagliapietra, Ed.D.**

Bob Jones University Press
Greenville, South Carolina 29614

**Student Activities in ALGEBRA 1 for Christian Schools®**

**Ron Tagliapietra, Ed.D.**

*for Christian Schools* is a registered trademark of Bob Jones University Press.

© 2000 Bob Jones University Press
Greenville, South Carolina 29614

Printed in the United States of America
All rights reserved

ISBN 1-57924-327-4

15   14   13   12   11   10   9   8   7   6   5   4   3   2

# Contents

# CHAPTER 1
*Integers*

## Bible: Numbers in Creation

**God created numbers during Creation week to describe the orderliness and exactness of His creation. Study the numbers in the Creation account.**

1. List the numbers in Genesis 1 that signal the end of a paragraph.

   _____

2. What do these numbers count? _____

3. Since God cannot do evil, what can you conclude about counting?

   _____

4. What other number do you find in Genesis 1? _____

5. What does this number describe? _____

6. Numbers describe both order of events and number of items. They are practical because they apply to a variety of things. What could you call

   this quality? _____

7. What number is repeated several times in Genesis 2? _____

8. What total can you find in Genesis 2:10? _____

9. God demonstrates that a total is a summary by counting the items one by

   one in Genesis 2:11-14. List the numbers used in the count. _____

   _____

10. What do these numbers describe? _____

11. What numbers occur in chapter 4? _____

    _____

12. What do the 28 numbers in chapter 5 describe? _____

The account of the great flood illustrates some other purposes for numbers.

13. Measurement. Give the dimensions of the ark (Gen. 6).

    _____

**14.** Specify quantities. How many of each creature did Noah count (Gen. 7)?

_____

**15.** Dates. Supply the first date from Genesis 7:11.

_____

**16.** Depth. Give the first depth (Gen. 7:20). _____

**17.** Chapter 8 also has a date; find it. _____

Numbers glorify God, describing the order and precision of God's creation. The Bible alone explains the creation of the earth in six days and the details of the flood.

**18.** What does Isaiah 55:9 say about God's knowledge?

_____

**19.** Write from memory Isaiah 55:9.

_____

_____

_____

# Math History: Eratosthenes

If you have not yet done the worksheet on *Prime Numbers,* do it now.

1. How does a knowledge of primes play an important role in factoring?

    _____

2. The method used to find the primes is named after Eratosthenes. What is

    it called? _____

3. When did Eratosthenes live? _____

4. Where was he from? _____

In his treatise *On the Measurement of the Earth,* Eratosthenes presented his calculation of the earth's circumference. Although his works no longer exist, we can learn some of the details of his works from other mathematicians, including Pappus, Heron, and Ptolemy.

5. What cities did Eratosthenes use as reference points when calculating the

    earth's circumference? _____

6. What circumference did he obtain? _____

7. This calculation was better than any other ancient estimate. What is the

    actual value? _____

8. He made other contributions to astronomy too. He determined that the earth is tilted 23° on its axis, and he suggested the modern (Julian) calendar by being the first to recommend that every fourth year comprise

    366 days. What do we call such years now? _____

9. Besides astronomy and mathematics, Eratosthenes achieved prominence in many other fields. Name at least two.

    _____

10. How and why did he die? _____

# Prime Numbers in Brief

## SIEVE OF ERATOSTHENES

Eratosthenes found an interesting way to find prime numbers. It is called the sieve of Eratosthenes. To find the primes from 1 to 100 according to his method, list the numbers. We have listed 1-30.

| 1 | 2 | 3 | 4 | 5 | 6 | 7 | 8 | 9 | 10 |
|---|---|---|---|---|---|---|---|---|---|
| 11 | 12 | 13 | 14 | 15 | 16 | 17 | 18 | 19 | 20 |
| 21 | 22 | 23 | 24 | 25 | 26 | 27 | 28 | 29 | 30 |

Circle the first prime number, which is 2. Now cross out every second number because it is not prime. Move to the next unmarked number, which is 3. Since 3 and 1 are its only factors, 3 is the next prime; circle it. Cross out every third number. Some will already be crossed out. Move to the next unmarked number. Since it is prime, circle it; then cross out all multiples of 5. When you finish crossing out multiples of 5, you will have all ten prime numbers between 1 and 30.

| 1 | 2 | 3 | 4 | 5 | 6 | 7 | 8 | 9 | 10 |
|---|---|---|---|---|---|---|---|---|---|
| 11 | 12 | 13 | 14 | 15 | 16 | 17 | 18 | 19 | 20 |
| 21 | 22 | 23 | 24 | 25 | 26 | 27 | 28 | 29 | 30 |

1. Finish marking your chart. Use the sieve of Eratosthenes to find all prime numbers between 2 and 100. How many are there? _____

| 1 | 2 | 3 | 4 | 5 | 6 | 7 | 8 | 9 | 10 |
|---|---|---|---|---|---|---|---|---|-----|
| 11 | 12 | 13 | 14 | 15 | 16 | 17 | 18 | 19 | 20 |
| 21 | 22 | 23 | 24 | 25 | 26 | 27 | 28 | 29 | 30 |
| 31 | 32 | 33 | 34 | 35 | 36 | 37 | 38 | 39 | 40 |
| 41 | 42 | 43 | 44 | 45 | 46 | 47 | 48 | 49 | 50 |
| 51 | 52 | 53 | 54 | 55 | 56 | 57 | 58 | 59 | 60 |
| 61 | 62 | 63 | 64 | 65 | 66 | 67 | 68 | 69 | 70 |
| 71 | 72 | 73 | 74 | 75 | 76 | 77 | 78 | 79 | 80 |
| 81 | 82 | 83 | 84 | 85 | 86 | 87 | 88 | 89 | 90 |
| 91 | 92 | 93 | 94 | 95 | 96 | 97 | 98 | 99 | 100 |

2. Twin primes are prime numbers that differ in value by 2. For example, 11 and 13 are twin primes. Find all twin primes between 1 and 100.

_____

3. List the primes between 100 and 200.

_____

_____

4. How many primes are there between 100 and 200?

_____

5. How many pairs of twin primes are between 100 and 200?

_____

6. At which multiple of 100 does the first pair of twin primes occur (one less, one more)?

_____

7. (optional) From 200 to 300 there are 16 primes and 4 pairs of twin primes. What are the lowest multiples of 100 between which there are no pairs of twin primes?

_____

# Integers Applied

## CHECKBOOKS

Mr. Conway made a mistake in his checkbook that he didn't notice until his bank statement came. He recorded all his transaction amounts correctly, but he miscalculated a balance. Correct his checkbook and be sure to show a $25 surcharge for every overdrawn check to be deducted at the end of the month.

| Date | Check no. | Transaction | Amount | Balance | Correction |
|------|-----------|-------------|--------|---------|------------|
| 7/30 | — | ending balance | — | $437 | |
| 8/2 | 674 | Palo Verde Apts. (rent) | −205 | 232 | |
| 8/3 | 675 | Swanson's Garage | −197 | 45 | |
| 8/4 | 676 | ABC Foodstore | −26 | 19 | |
| 8/4 | 677 | Ben's Gas Station | −11 | 8 | |
| 8/5 | — | Paycheck | +326 | 334 | |
| 8/7 | 678 | Waterville Church | −50 | 284 | |
| 8/10 | 679 | Northern Electric Co. | −39 | 245 | |
| 8/10 | 680 | Northern Bell Telephone | −57 | 188 | |
| 8/11 | 681 | ABC Food | −85 | 103 | |
| 8/15 | 682 | Dr. Walters | −92 | 11 | |
| 8/19 | — | Paycheck | +326 | 337 | |
| 8/21 | 683 | Waterville Church | −50 | 287 | |
| 8/22 | 684 | ABC Food | −69 | 218 | |
| 8/22 | 685 | Ben's Gas Station | −12 | 206 | |
| 8/24 | 686 | Waterville Travel Agency | −200 | 6 | |
| 8/27 | — | Transfer from Savings | +150 | 156 | |
| 8/28 | 687 | Quick Stop Shop | −23 | 133 | |
| 8/28 | 688 | Waterville Drug | −15 | 118 | |
| 8/28 | 689 | Western Water Co. | −43 | 75 | |
| 8/28 | 690 | Riverway Books | −11 | 64 | |

1. How much did his error cost him? _____

2. What does a negative transaction amount mean?

   _____

3. What does a negative balance mean? _____

4. How could you avoid Mr. Conway's problem? _____

   _____

# ■ Practice

*INTEGER OPERATIONS*

**Add.**

| | |
|---|---|
| _____ **1.** $18 + 11$ | _____ **6.** $46 + (-52)$ |
| _____ **2.** $27 + (-5)$ | _____ **7.** $37 + 16$ |
| _____ **3.** $-36 + 16$ | _____ **8.** $-11 + (-8)$ |
| _____ **4.** $-41 + 73$ | _____ **9.** $0 + 8$ |
| _____ **5.** $-16 + (-5)$ | _____ **10.** $-42 + 32$ |

**Subtract.**

| | |
|---|---|
| _____ **11.** $251 - 73$ | _____ **16.** $17 - 5$ |
| _____ **12.** $91 - (-12)$ | _____ **17.** $(-19) - 36$ |
| _____ **13.** $-87 - 15$ | _____ **18.** $(-8) - (-11)$ |
| _____ **14.** $16 - 50$ | _____ **19.** $41 - (-60)$ |
| _____ **15.** $-22 - (-17)$ | _____ **20.** $-11 - 20$ |

**Multiply.**

| | |
|---|---|
| _____ **21.** $11 \cdot 6$ | _____ **26.** $-20(-7)$ |
| _____ **22.** $(23)(-5)$ | _____ **27.** $(-21)(14)$ |
| _____ **23.** $31 \cdot 15$ | _____ **28.** $7(-12)$ |
| _____ **24.** $12(-8)$ | _____ **29.** $16(0)$ |
| _____ **25.** $-6(5)$ | _____ **30.** $1(-38)$ |

**Divide.**

| | |
|---|---|
| _____ **31.** $-39 \div 3$ | _____ **36.** $312 \div 12$ |
| _____ **32.** $0 \div 11$ | _____ **37.** $-300 \div 6$ |
| _____ **33.** $28 \div (-7)$ | _____ **38.** $-448 \div (-32)$ |
| _____ **34.** $88 \div 4$ | _____ **39.** $50 \div (-1)$ |
| _____ **35.** $-18 \div (-2)$ | _____ **40.** $476 \div (-68)$ |

**Simplify.**

_____ **41.** $159 + (-53)$      _____ **46.** $(-21) - (-9)$

_____ **42.** $159 \div (-53)$      _____ **47.** $-21(-9)$

_____ **43.** $23(0)$      _____ **48.** $-163 + (-21)$

_____ **44.** $-15 \cdot 3$      _____ **49.** $264 \div 66$

_____ **45.** $-36 - 5$      _____ **50.** $0 - 7$

# ■ Practice ··········································································································

## *TRANSLATING*

_____   **1.** Translate "five less than seven."

**2.** What property guarantees that 5 + 7 and 7 + 5 are the same number?

_____

**3.** Which is the more literal translation of "five more than seven"? Why?

_____

_____   **4.** The word "than" signals a comparison. In both "more than" and "less than," do you put the base of comparison (the word after "than") first or last in your translation?

_____   **5.** In "five less seven" the word "than" is absent. How is this translated?

Be careful of opposites; exponents are done before signs. $-3^2$ means $-(3^2) = -9$. If you want to square $-3$ you need parentheses $(-3)^2 = (-3)(-3) = 9$.

**Translate each phrase. Do not calculate.**

_____   **6.** The opposite of five

_____   **7.** The opposite of negative eleven

_____   **8.** The absolute value of negative four

_____   **9.** The sum of negative two and three

_____   **10.** The quotient of twenty and seven

_____   **11.** The difference of six and negative ten

_____   **12.** The product of twenty-four and twelve

_____   **13.** The square of six

_____   **14.** The fourth power of nineteen

_____   **15.** The opposite of the cube of five

_____   **16.** Six plus the square of negative one

_____   **17.** Negative five times negative eight

_____   **18.** Fourteen divided by three

_____   **19.** Twenty decreased by the absolute value of negative three

_____ **20.** Ten squared added to negative four

_____ **21.** Seven groups of negative four

_____ **22.** The absolute value of the difference between two and four

_____ **23.** Seventeen more than the opposite of six

_____ **24.** The square of negative eight less the absolute value of nine

_____ **25.** Zero less five cubed

# CHAPTER 2
## *Real Numbers*

## Bible: Numbers in Haggai

**1.** Read Haggai and make a list of every number you find. Give its reference and the thing that is numbered. Be sure to include zero ("none" or "no one").

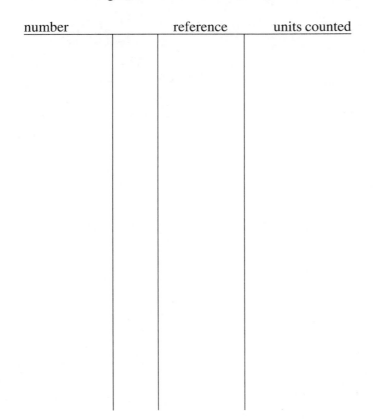

number          reference          units counted

**2.** How many numbers did you find in this short book of two chapters?

_____

**3.** What was the purpose of most of the numbers in the book?

_____

**4.** What kind of numbers were they? _____

**5.** All but one of the numbers can be classified as what kind of number?

_____

**6.** What kind of number do you think is the most frequent type in the Bible?

_____

**7.** Review Romans 3:10. What special number was used in this verse? Explain.

_____

# Math History

## *MODERN SYMBOLS INTRODUCED BEFORE 1600*

Use encyclopedias (reference mathematics history) or books on the history of mathematics from your library to answer the questions about the development of our modern symbols.

**1.** Our numerals 1, 2, 3, . . . , 9 appeared first in the Western (Greek-speaking) world in 662. In that year Severus Sebokt told the West about the place value system of the group of people who first used place value numeration. Leonardo of Pisa, or Fibonacci, popularized the principle of place value in the 13th century. Name the group who first used it.

_____

**2.** The shapes of our numbers developed from another group of people.

Which group? _____

**3.** This last group of people also used fraction bars. All of these meant two-thirds: 2/3; 2-3; $\frac{2}{3}$. Which is no longer used as a fraction symbol? _____

Johann Widman published a book in 1489 that used the $+$ and $-$ symbols for the first time. These symbols were not really used at that time to indicate the operations of addition and subtraction but rather to indicate excess and deficiency. By 1514, $+$ and $-$ were being used to indicate operations and were used quite often by Vander Hoeckie, a mathematician from the Netherlands. The minus sign may have come from the symbol $\overline{m}$, meaning minus.

**4.** From where did the plus sign orginate? _____

The radical sign $\sqrt{\phantom{x}}$ is the symbol for the principal (positive) square root. One of the earliest works to make use of this sign was the *Coss* by Christoph L. Rudolph, published in 1525.

**5.** From where did the radical sign originate? _____

_____

The equal sign was introduced in *The Whetstone of Witte* by Robert Recorde.

**6.** What year was this published? _____

Rafaello Bombelli of Italy published a book in 1572 that used a capital *L* and a reversed *L* ($\llcorner$) to enclose expressions. His procedure may have suggested the use of brackets.

**7.** When did Bombelli live? _____

## *Calculator Skills* —————————————

### ORDER OF OPERATIONS

How does the order of operations apply to using calculators? Use parentheses keys to compute the following expressions. Enter each symbol in the order shown (if a symbol is written above a calculator key instead of on the key, you must press the [ 2nd ], [ Shift ], or [ INV ] key before you press the key that you want).

$(5 + 6) \cdot 8 =$        $5 + (6 \cdot 8) =$

The first calculation above gets 88, the second 53. Now, compute $5 + 6 \cdot 8 =$ without any parentheses. Which answer does it match? Did your calculator evaluate the operations in the order they were entered (answer 88), or did it follow the mathematical order of operations (answer 53)? This exercise tells you when you do not need parentheses and when you must be careful. You will find it less confusing if your calculator follows the same priorities of order as math—otherwise you have to know two systems!

Now use the [ $x^2$ ] button. Notice the order again:

$5 + 3^2$        $5^2 + 3$        $5^2 + 3^2$        $(5 + 3)^2$

The answer to these four problems should be 14, 28, 34, and 64 respectively. If you used parentheses only on the fourth problem, the calculator is following the mathematical order. Be sure that you know when to use parentheses to get the right answers on your calculator.

Practice using your calculator with real numbers. You will need to use the decimal point key to enter many of these numbers. Some calculators may not permit parentheses inside parentheses. If your calculator gives errors, you may calculate from the inside out. Round answers, where applicable, to the nearest thousandth.

_____  **1.** $27 + 15 \cdot 9$

_____  **2.** $95.7 \div 8.2 + 6$

_____  **3.** $111.3 - 88 \div 6$

_____  **4.** $53.1 - 2.1 + 4.3$

_____  **5.** $46.4^2 + 2 \cdot 7.6$

_____  **6.** $7.4 + 1.3 \cdot 5.6^2$

_____  **7.** $3 \cdot (5.7 - 11.2)^2 + 4$

_____  **8.** $2.8 - 7.5^2 \cdot 3.4$

_____  **9.** $3(2.8 - 7.6(19.1 + 3.2))$

_____ **10.** $14^2 + 2.7(5.1 - 3.8)^2 + 1$

_____ **11.** $(((3.7 - 8.1)4 - 6.7)4.5 + 3.2)7.1 + 11.2^2$

**12.** How many sets of parentheses does your calculator allow? (One set, 3 sets, 10 sets, and 12 sets are common.) _____

# Estimation in Brief

## BASIC SKILLS

You shouldn't need to show any work on these; do them in your head.

Estimate each value by rounding the numbers before performing the operations.

_____ **1.** $29 + 13(-78)$     _____ **6.** $96.11 - 19.9$

_____ **2.** $55 \cdot 42 - 653$     _____ **7.** $(77)^2 - 33 \cdot 80$

_____ **3.** $2768 - 9^3$     _____ **8.** $289 \div (37 + 56)$

_____ **4.** $88 \cdot 96 \div 17$     _____ **9.** $\frac{562}{49} - 33 \cdot 11$

_____ **5.** $21 + 889 \div 57$     _____ **10.** $68 \cdot 14 - 92 \cdot 63$

Give the closest whole number.

_____ **11.** $\sqrt{19}$     _____ **16.** $\sqrt{160}$

_____ **12.** $\sqrt{35}$     _____ **17.** $\sqrt[3]{9}$

_____ **13.** $\sqrt{130}$     _____ **18.** $\sqrt[3]{121}$

_____ **14.** $\sqrt{5}$     _____ **19.** $\sqrt[4]{100}$

_____ **15.** $\sqrt{54}$     _____ **20.** $\sqrt[4]{4}$

Give the closest multiple of ten.

_____ **21.** $4.7 \cdot 6.1$     _____ **26.** $7.43 + 17.11$

_____ **22.** $19.25 - 8.42$     _____ **27.** $8.36 \div 2.11$

_____ **23.** $21.5 \cdot 4.3$     _____ **28.** $11.6(10.4)$

_____ **24.** $28 \div 3.7$     _____ **29.** $19.9(3.4)$

_____ **25.** $77.69 - 11.88$     _____ **30.** $97.86 + 67.98$

# Real Numbers Applied

## BUDGETS

A business executive collected some information on expenses for his upcoming budget meeting. You are to make two visual aids for him.

1. The first is a display of the current year's budget as a pie graph. Calculate the percentage of the whole for each entry. Determine the angle (percentage • 360) that will represent each entry. Draw the graph.

1999 Expenditures:

| | |
|---|---|
| Advertising | $23,510 |
| Building costs & maintenance | $47,010 |
| Office materials | $23,540 |
| Raw materials | $47,180 |
| Employee wages | $70,670 |
| Taxes | $23,590 |

Total: $235,500

2. What three expenditures make up almost 3/4 of the budget?

_____

For each question below, give the answer and tell which operation was needed to compute the answer.

3. How much more was spent on raw materials than office materials?

_____

4. How much was spent in total on materials this year?

_____

5. How many times larger is the largest part of the budget than the smallest part?

_____

6. The executive committee plans a 4% cost of living increase for all employees. How much should the budget for next year include for wages?

_____

7. Raw materials and office materials are expected to increase 7%. How much should be budgeted for each?

_____

8. The building rent will increase $100 per month and the maintenance contract will increase $349 for the year. What should be budgeted for building costs & maintenance?

_____

**9.** The committee previously determined to keep the budget down to $250,000 based on revenue trends. They plan $25,000 in taxes on this basis. What can their expenditures be for advertising to keep a balanced budget?

_____

**10.** Calculate the percentages and angle degrees, and draw a pie graph for the next year's budget.

2000 Expenditures:

| | |
|---|---|
| Advertising | $27,273.80 |
| Building costs & maintenance | $48,559.00 |
| Office materials | $25,187.80 |
| Raw materials | $50,482.60 |
| Employee wages | $73,496.80 |
| Taxes | $25,000.00 |
| | Total: $250,000.00 |

# CHAPTER 3
## *The Language of Algebra*

## Bible: Variables

A variable is an abstract idea. Sometimes we avoid abstractions because they seem difficult; however, abstractions increase man's understanding and problem solving skills. Let's think of some abstract ideas in the Bible. Use a dictionary and a concordance.

1. What does it mean to *abstract* metal from ore? _____

2. What is an abstraction?

   _____

3. Explain how "red" is an abstraction by naming three different physical objects that are red in the Bible. Include references.

   _____

   _____

4. Notice that the word "color" is a variable that includes the abstraction "red." Find a Bible chapter that uses the abstract variable "color" and that names three specific colors in connection. _____

5. Explain that "nineteen" is an abstraction by naming three different items of which the Bible records nineteen. Include references.

   _____

   _____

6. What word is a variable that includes each abstract quantity like "19"? Our letter variables provide means for translating this word into symbols.

   _____

You have studied a grammatical variable "whosoever" in this chapter. This reminds us that variables enable us to summarize information.

7. Use a grammatical variable to summarize the following list of facts:

   In Tokyo there are twenty-four hours in a day.

   In Miami there are twenty-four hours in a day.

   In Madrid there are twenty-four hours in a day.

   In Capetown there are twenty-four hours in a day.

   _____

8. Name another grammatical variable and find it in the Bible.

   _____

9. Summarize the following list using math variables. What do you call the generalization?

   $2 + 3 = 3 + 2$

   $5 + 7 = 7 + 5$         _____

   $\frac{1}{2} + 10 = 10 + \frac{1}{2}$

   $\sqrt{2} + 5.4 = 5.4 + \sqrt{2}$

10. Review John 3:16 as a memory verse. Which word is the variable?

    _____

# Math History: Al-Khwarizmi

The history of algebra traces to a number of sources. Hindu numeration systems for calculating, as in the writings of Brahmagupta, form one important influence. Greek geometric problem solving as in Euclid also provides a tool for justifying solutions. However, these various influences came together in the writings of Mohammed ibn-Musa al-Khwarizmi. His name is also spelled al-Khowarizmi and Alkarismi.

1. In which century did al-Khwarizmi die? _____

2. Where was he from? _____

3. His name has been contracted into a modern English word for a computational procedure. What is the word named after him?

   _____

Al-Khwarizmi wrote a number of important books. One of his books introduced the Hindu calculation systems to Europe. Only a Latin translation of his Arabic book survives.

4. What is the name of this influential book?

   _____

Another of his books laid the foundation for modern algebraic solutions of equations.

5. Name the book. _____

6. Give the part of the title that became a mathematical term. What is the

   English word? _____

7. The original meaning of this title is not clear, but it probably refers to "restoring and balancing" by operating on both sides. What principle permits

   us to keep equations balanced? _____

8. Can you recognize which of the following equations could be solved using his book?

   $$x^2 + 5x = 36, \quad x^3 = |x|, \quad 3^x = 5, \quad 3x = 12, \quad \frac{5}{x} = x^2$$

   _____

9. On this basis some say that this man is the father of what mathematical

   subject? _____

## Calculator Skills

### SCIENTIFIC NOTATION

How many digits can you enter on your calculator? Some calculators can fit only an eight-digit number. Perhaps yours takes twelve digits—but what if you need to calculate this?

18,357,600,000,000 ÷ 836.72159

Scientific notation will help. Do you remember how to write numbers in scientific notation as you learned in earlier grades? Put the decimal after the first digit and multiply by the correct power of 10.

$1.83576 \times 10^{13} \div 8.3672159 \times 10^2$

On your calculator enter 1.83576 **EXP** 13. You may have an **EE** or **SCI** key to represent the scientific notation instead of **EXP** (exponential notation). Notice that the 13 is separated from the rest of the number by spaces. The 13 by itself is the calculator's way of telling you that the number must be multiplied by $10^{13}$. Now press **÷** and enter 8.3672159 **EXP** 2 **=**. Did you get $2.19399 \times 10^{10}$?

Now do $3.8 \times 10^{17} \cdot 4.9 \times 10^{12} \cdot 5.7 \times 10^{41} \div 9.53 \times 10^{23}$. The answer is $1.11368 \times 10^{48}$, but suppose you typed 5.6 instead of 5.7 by mistake. Do you have to start all over? If you recognize your mistake before you press **÷**, you can touch **CE** to *clear entry*. This erases only your $5.6 \times 10^{41}$ entry and lets you retype it without losing the previous calculations. There are three main types of erase buttons.

**→** (arrow key) erases one digit at a time from right to left, but does not erase the exponent in scientific notation.

**CE** or **C** (clear entry) erases only the current entry.

**C** or **AC** (clear) erases the whole problem, but not things stored in memory (which you will learn about soon).

Use scientific notation to calculate:

_____ **1.** What is 23,962,500,000,000 · 753,962,140,000,000?

_____ **2.** What is 0.00000046928 ÷ 8,350,000,000,000?

_____ **3.** What is $3.6 \times 10^{-12} + 4.9 \times 10^{-11}$?

4. Find $2^2$, $(2^2)^2$, $[(2^2)^2]^2$, and so on. What is the first square that has an answer in scientific notation? _____

   _____

   What is the first one that overflows the calculator?

   _____

5. Why is it easier to do $(1 \times 10^{5000}) \cdot (1 \times 10^{8000})$ in your head than on a calculator? What's the answer?

   _____

   _____

   _____

_____   6.  $(2.87 \times 10^{68}) - (5.9182 \times 10^{70})$

_____   7.  $5.3 \times 10^{-41} - 1.04 \times 10^{-39}$

Repeat exercise 6 or 7 but make a mistake and correct it in the

8. second number part.

9. second exponent.

10. operation.

# Solutions in Brief:  Estimation and Context

An answer is given for each problem below. Your job is to check each answer mentally and rate its appropriateness. First, check the context of the answer. The answer may be mathematically *impossible* in the context, or *unrealistic* in defying common sense. If the context checks, then mentally approximate the answer and rate the answer: *overprecise* if the answer is more precise than given information permits, *inaccurate* if the estimate is poor, or *reasonable*.

**Use *D* = *rt* for problems 1-5.**

1. How far does a car go if it travels 13 hours at 55 mph? $\sqrt{700}$ mi.

_____

2. How far does a car go traveling 47 mph for 9 hours? 420 mi.  _____

3. How far does a car go in 41 hours at 53 mph? 3000 mi.  _____

4. How far does a car go at 25 mph in 14 hours? 357 mi.

5. How far does a car go in 17.2 hours at 54 mph? 100 mi.

_____

6. How much does 2.4 lb. of fruit at $1.26 per lb. cost? $25

_____

7. How much does 5.7 lbs. of nuts at $0.65 per lb. cost? $10^4$

_____

8. How much does 11 lbs. of vegetables at $1.30 per lb. cost? $13.43

_____

9. How much are 8.9 lbs of fruit at $0.73 per lb.? $6.50  _____

10. How much are 2.9 lbs. of nuts at $2.19 per lb.? $7.30

_____

**Continue the process for the areas of rectangles given below.**

11. 4.7 yds. by 6.2 yds.   28 sq. yds. _____

12. 13.4 ft. by 19.8 ft.   66 sq. ft. _____

13. 1.34 miles by 1.62 miles   −4 sq. mi. _____

**14.** 17.1 meters by 18.2 meters   20 sq. meters

_____

**15.** 234 in. by 593 in.   1640.8 sq. in.

_____

## Formulas Applied: Profits

The bar graph below shows the profits for the Bible Book Store over a ten-year period.

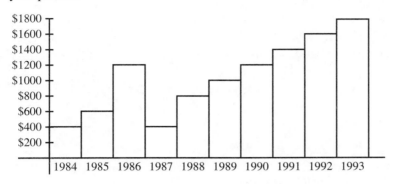

_____ **1.** The profits of the Bible Book Store have been increasing since what year?

_____ **2.** How much did the store earn in 1990?

_____ **3.** In what year did the store make $600 profit?

_____ **4.** What year showed the biggest increase over the previous year?

_____ **5.** How much did the store's profits increase from 1992 to 1993?

The Crown Cabinet Company wants to make a profit graph similar to the one on the previous page. Look at the table below of their total costs for the last five years, their cabinet selling price during each year, and the number of cabinets sold each year.

| | $C$<br>Total costs | $S$<br>Selling price | $x$<br>Number of |
|---|---|---|---|
| Year | (dollars) | per cabinet (dollars) | cabinets sold |
| 1989 | $1237.46 | $89.95 | 252 |
| 1990 | $1553.11 | $92.95 | 289 |
| 1991 | $1872.34 | $95.95 | 312 |
| 1992 | $1825.75 | $95.99 | 293 |
| 1993 | $1949.82 | $99.99 | 307 |

6. Use the formula $R = Sx$ to find the total revenue (income) for each year.

7. Use the formula $P = R - C$ to find the total profit for each year.

8. Now make a bar graph for the profits of the Crown Cabinet Company for these five years. What is the total profit?

---

## Exponents in Detail: Positive and Negative Exponents

1.  What does $5 \cdot 3$ mean? It means $3 + 3 + 3 + 3 + 3$; add five terms of three. Use this idea to complete the meaning column in the table below. By the time you get to $0 \cdot 3$, you should be able to complete the pattern.

    What is it? _____

    Complete the column. Notice that $-2 \cdot 3$ means to UNDO three times two. "Undo" in this case means to undo the repeated addition. This is why you have to start subtracting threes toward the bottom. Because it is repeated ADDITION, $0 \cdot 3$ means no terms of three; we are at the base point for addition.

2.  What is this base point called? _____

3.  When we start undoing the additions we use $-3$ instead of $+3$. What is

    the property that relates them? _____

4.  Now complete the result column. Notice that the same pattern develops as you progress down this column.

| problem | meaning | result |
|---------|---------|--------|
| $5 \cdot 3$ | $3 + 3 + 3 + 3 + 3$ | 15 |
| $4 \cdot 3$ | | |
| $3 \cdot 3$ | | |
| $2 \cdot 3$ | | |
| $1 \cdot 3$ | | |
| $0 \cdot 3$ | | |
| $-1 \cdot 3$ | | |
| $-2 \cdot 3$ | | |
| $-3 \cdot 3$ | | |
| $-4 \cdot 3$ | | |

The three reasons that $0 \cdot 3 = 0$ are the pattern in the meaning column, the pattern in the result column, and the role of the additive identity as a base point for repeated addition.

Three reasons for the meaning of negative products of three are the patterns in the meaning and result column and the role of the additive inverse of three for undoing repeated additions.

5.  Now, what does $3^5$ mean? It means $3 \cdot 3 \cdot 3 \cdot 3 \cdot 3$; multiply five factors of three. Use this idea to make a problem/meaning/result table like the one above relating exponents to multiplication. Again, give three reasons each for your conclusions regarding zero and negative exponents.

# ■ Practice

*EQUATIONS*

**If *I* = *Prt*, find *I* if**

_____  **1.** $P = 100, r = 0.08, t = 2.$

_____  **2.** $P = 20, r = 0.10, t = 1.$

_____  **3.** $P = 200, r = 0.06, t = 4.$

_____  **4.** $P = 500, r = 0.07, t = 10.$

_____  **5.** $P = 800, r = 0.05, t = \frac{1}{2}.$

**Use formulas to answer each question.**

**6.** What is the perimeter of a rectangular farm that is 3 miles long by $1\frac{3}{4}$ miles wide? _____

**7.** The top of a circular water tower has a diameter of 50 ft. How long should the guardrail be? ($C = \pi d$) _____

**8.** How far does a jet travel in 3 hours at 217 mph? ($D = rt$) _____

**9.** How much wallpaper is needed to cover a triangle 10 feet long and 8 feet high to be used as a stage prop? $\left(A = \frac{1}{2}bh\right)$ _____

**10.** How much space is required to store a package in the shape of a pyramid 9 inches tall and having a square base with sides 6 inches long? $\left(V = \frac{1}{3}s^2h\right)$ _____

**Identify each property if *a* = *b*.**

**11.** $a + 6 = b + 6$ _____

**12.** $a - a = b - a$ _____

**13.** $ma = mb$ _____

**14.** $\frac{a}{3} = \frac{b}{3}$ _____

**15.** $a + k = b + k$ _____

**Translate each sentence into an equation.**

_____  **16.** Seven more than twice a number is nine.

_____  **17.** Four times a number equals five minus the number.

_____  **18.** Three times the square of a number is six.

_____  **19.** The opposite of a number is twice the number.

_____  **20.** Nineteen less half a number is twenty.

_____  **21.** Seven-thirds of a number subtracted from one-half is three-halves.

_____  **22.** The sum of two consecutive numbers is ninety-nine.

_____  **23.** Twelve is the square of twice a number.

_____  **24.** The product of two consecutive even numbers is twenty more than the larger.

_____  **25.** The reciprocal of a number is the same as the square root of the number.

# ■ Cumulative Review

_____ 1. Factor 108 into primes.

_____ 2. Find the LCM of 20 and 35.

_____ 3. Find $\{-3, 2, 5, 7\} \cap \{-3, -1, 1, 3, 5\}$.

_____ 4. Use $C = \frac{5}{9}(F - 32°)$ to convert 77°F to centigrade.

_____ 5. What kind of number is 3.14?

**Simplify.**

_____ 6. $2 + (-1)$

_____ 7. $-8(-3)$

_____ 8. $4x - 9x$

_____ 9. $\frac{2}{3} - \frac{1}{5}$

_____ 10. $-7 - (-2)$

_____ 11. $\frac{12}{5} \cdot \frac{25}{14}$

_____ 12. $27 \div (-3)$

_____ 13. $5(x - 6)$

_____ 14. $3 + 2 \cdot 6$

_____ 15. $8 - 3(2 + 4)$

_____ 16. $|-3|$

_____ 17. $5^8 \div 5^5$

_____ 18. $2^{-1}$

_____ 19. $\sqrt{36}$

_____ 20. $4^0 + |4| + \sqrt{4}$

**Evaluate for $x = 3$, $y = -4$.**

_____ 21. $x + y$

_____ 22. $x^2 - xy$

**Identify each property. Assume** *a* = *b*.

**23.** $5(a - 3) = 5a - 15$ _____

**24.** $2^3 \cdot 2^4 = 2^7$ _____

**25.** $\frac{a}{5} = \frac{b}{5}$ _____

**26.** $1 \cdot a = a$ _____

**27.** $0 \cdot a = 0$ _____

**28.** $a + 7 = b + 7$ _____

**29.** $a - a = 0$ _____

**30.** $a - a = b - a$ _____

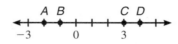

_____  **31.** Give the coordinates of *A* and *D*.

_____  **32.** Give the midpoint of *BC*.

**Translate each phrase or sentence.**

_____  **33.** Five more than a number

_____  **34.** Subtract 12 from thirty.

_____  **35.** Seven less than a number is nineteen.

_____  **36.** The sum of two consecutive numbers

_____  **37.** The product of five and the square of a number

_____  **38.** Two divided into ten is five.

_____  **39.** The total points made by a basketball player
who makes *x* free throws, *y* two-point baskets,
and *z* three-point shots

**40.** Write Romans 3:10 from memory. _____

_____

_____

# CHAPTER 4
## Solving Equations

## Bible: Whole Numbers in Old Testament History

There are numbers in every book of the Bible except Lamentations and III John. In the next few Bible projects you will verify this fact. Keep good records because you will refer to these in later Bible projects.

In this project you will find natural numbers in every historical book of the Old Testament. Look up the verse, write all the numbers you find in the verse, and give the units or objects that they measure. This will help you see the importance of the contexts and uses of numbers.

|     | Book         | Verse | Numbers | Objects |
| --- | ------------ | ----- | ------- | ------- |
| 1.  | Genesis      | 37:2  |         |         |
| 2.  | Exodus       | 38:24 |         |         |
| 3.  | Leviticus    | 23:34 |         |         |
| 4.  | Numbers      | 7:84  |         |         |
| 5.  | Deuteronomy  | 34:8  |         |         |
| 6.  | Joshua       | 15:54 |         |         |
| 7.  | Judges       | 10:8  |         |         |
| 8.  | Ruth         | 1:4   |         |         |
| 9.  | I Samuel     | 4:15  |         |         |
| 10. | II Samuel    | 2:30  |         |         |
| 11. | I Kings      | 16:8  |         |         |
| 12. | II Kings     | 15:1  |         |         |
| 13. | I Chronicles | 4:27  |         |         |
| 14. | II Chronicles| 33:21 |         |         |
| 15. | Ezra         | 8:11  |         |         |
| 16. | Nehemiah     | 6:15  |         |         |
| 17. | Esther       | 9:17  |         |         |

**18.** Review Luke 15:4. Which numbers did it contain? _____

## Math History: Alhazen

Alhazen was an Arabic mathematician and physicist. How much can you find out about Alhazen?

1. The name Alhazen is the English name that we know him by, but how is his name more correctly written? _____

2. During approximately which years did he live? _____

3. In what country did he live? _____

4. What was his most famous book? _____

   _____

5. What famous Greek thinkers influenced Alhazen's work?

   _____

6. Name at least one problem that Alhazen studied.

   _____

   _____

   _____

7. Omar Khayyam was another Arabic mathematician. Write a paragraph about him.

   _____

   _____

   _____

   _____

   _____

8. Name another Arabic mathematician and write a sentence about him.

   _____

   _____

   _____

# Equations in Brief: Estimation Skills

Without solving the following problems, decide how many solutions there should be and what the sign of the answers should be.

_____   **1.** $-3.7x = -5.2$

_____   **2.** $x + 8.1 = 4.7$

_____   **3.** $35x - 17 = 205$

_____   **4.** $|23x - 15| = 12$

_____   **5.** $-3.7x + 6.4 = 9.3$

_____   **6.** $4.157x + 7.239 = 5.162$

_____   **7.** $|4.12x + 2.31| = 1.38$

_____   **8.** $2.96x - 3.47 = 6.59 + 3.22x$

_____   **9.** $14.37x + 14.29 = 11.37x + 10.55$

_____   **10.** $\frac{2x}{5} - \frac{3}{7} = \frac{x}{10}$

_____   **11.** $|4.7x + 2.1| = 0$

_____   **12.** $3.96(5.2x - 3.1) = 7.2 - x$

_____   **13.** $4.1(2.1x + 5) = 7.9x + 17.8$

_____   **14.** $|3.2x - 5.1| + 3.7 = 9.5$

_____   **15.** $15 - \frac{x}{12} = 23$

_____   **16.** $2.5 - 3(4.1 + x) = 3.7$

_____   **17.** $91.8 = 7.3 - 15x$

_____   **18.** $\frac{4.329x}{5.76} = 4.86x$

_____   **19.** $|5.3x - 8.1| = 1.2$

_____   **20.** $6.2 - 5.6x = 7.3x + 9.1$

# Equations Applied: Auto Race

Ten men participated in an auto race from Orlando, FL, to Seattle, WA. The two five-man relay teams each selected the route they thought would be fastest.

George left Orlando on the Florida Turnpike and took I-75 to I-10. He stayed on I-10 through Mobile, AL, and New Orleans, LA, until he came to Baton Rouge. Phil continued on I-10 to Houston, TX, took I-45 into Dallas, and then I-35 up to Oklahoma City. Larry continued the drive to Wichita, KS, where he used I-135 to connect to I-70. When he reached Denver, CO, he caught I-25 up to Cheyenne, WY. Glen left Cheyenne on I-80 to Twin Falls, ID. Randy continued on I-84 but switched to I-82 just past Pendleton, OR. I-82 joins I-90 to go into Seattle.

Meanwhile, John was taking I-75 up to Chattanooga, TN. There he got on I-24 for Nashville. Rick continued via I-24, I-57, and I-64 to St. Louis, where he got on I-70 for Kansas City, MO. Jeff drove up I-29 to Sioux Falls, SD, and then turned west on I-90 for Rapid City. Pete continued on I-90 all the way to Butte, MT. Andy drove the last leg of I-90 into Seattle.

Including gas stops, Glen, Pete, and Randy were able to average 60 mph in the wide open west. Four drivers could average only 55 because the highways passed through the metropolitan areas of Denver, Houston, Atlanta, and Omaha. Dense fog on the river crossing from Kentucky to Illinois and accidents around Biloxi, MS, and Spokane, WA, caused three drivers to average only 50 mph.

John, Glen, Rick, and Andy all drove for the same amount of time. Jeff, George, and Phil each drove one hour longer than Glen. Larry drove one hour less than Glen, whereas Pete drove two hours less than Glen. Randy drove an hour and a half less than Glen. If the total distance driven by the ten drivers was 6495 miles, which team won?

## Equations in Detail: Inverse Operations

You know at least seven processes now. You also know how to undo them. Let's review.

| Process | description | Inverse | description |
|---|---|---|---|
| $+ n$ | add a number | $- n$ | subtract the number |
| $- n$ | subtract a number | $+ n$ | add the number |
| $\cdot n$ | multiply by a number | $\div n$ | divide by the number |
| $\div n$ | divide by a number | $\cdot n$ | multiply by the number |
| $(\ \ )^2$ | square | $\sqrt{\ \ }$ | square root; two possible answers—positive or negative |
| $\sqrt{\ \ }$ | square root | $(\ \ )^2$ | square |
| $\vert\ \vert$ | absolute value | | remove bars by writing two equations |

You also know the order of operations and that you must undo them in reverse order to solve an equation, just as you remove your shoes before your socks, though you put your socks on first. In $5x - 2 = 1$, you undo the $-2$ by adding 2 before you reverse the multiplication by 5 through division.

See if you can solve these equations by using these principles.

1. $|x| = 8$

2. $x^2 = 16$

3. $\sqrt{x} = 7$

4. $5|x| - 1 = 9$

5. $x^2 - 8 = 17$

6. $\sqrt{x} + 1 = 3$

7. $5|x - 2| + 4 = 9$

8. $3\sqrt{x} + 2 = 5$

9. $5x^2 - 2 = 18$

10. $5\sqrt{x} - 2 = 15$

11. $\sqrt{x^2 - 5} = 2$

12. $(3x + 1)^2 = 100$

13. $8 + 3|2x - 1| = 14$

14. $\sqrt{3x^2 + 9} = 6$

15. $\sqrt{6 + 2|x|} = 4$

Now see if you can write solutions in words for these problems.

**16.** Five more than the square root of a number is 11.

_____

**17.** Four less than twice the square of a number is 28.

_____

**18.** Suppose piquon is the inverse process of vimev. The vimev of 3 less than a number is 20. _____

**19.** Suppose log is the inverse process for pow. The pow of one-fourth of the number is 53. _____

**20.** Suppose natlog is the inverse process for expon, and tan is the inverse process for arctan. The arctan of the natlog of a number is 40.

_____

# ■ Practice

## LINEAR EQUATIONS

**Solve.**

_____  **1.** $x + 5 = 1$          _____  **6.** $4 + x = 3$

_____  **2.** $x - 3 = 10$          _____  **7.** $3 - x = 8$

_____  **3.** $3x = -8$          _____  **8.** $-\frac{x}{3} = -6$

_____  **4.** $\frac{x}{4} = 12$          _____  **9.** $-2x = -10$

_____  **5.** $-7x = 56$          _____  **10.** $7x = -11$

_____  **11.** $3y + 2 = 5$          _____  **16.** $-2p + 3 = 5$

_____  **12.** $7x + 6 = 6$          _____  **17.** $-x - 3 = 8$

_____  **13.** $2t - 1 = -5$          _____  **18.** $-11q + 100 = -21$

_____  **14.** $-3m + 4 = 13$          _____  **19.** $6r - 5 = 3$

_____  **15.** $4n + 2 = 5$          _____  **20.** $-2z + 3 = 7$

_____  **21.** $5x + 3x = -24$

_____  **22.** $7x - 2(x + 3) = 19$

_____  **23.** $-2x + 3(x - 4) = -20$

_____  **24.** $4(x - 2) - 3(x + 1) = 10$

_____  **25.** $5(2x + 3) = 7$

_____  **26.** $3 - 2(x + 8) = -5$

_____  **27.** $-6 + 3(x - 5) = -15$

_____  **28.** $11 + 4x - 8 = 27$

_____  **29.** $3(2x + 4) = 12$

_____  **30.** $6(3x - 2) - 5(2x + 3) = -35$

# ■ Practice ......................................................

## *EQUATIONS*

**Solve.**

_____ **1.** $5x + 9 = 3x + 15$   _____ **6.** $3(x + 4) = 2x + 1$

_____ **2.** $8x - 6 = 4x - 7$   _____ **7.** $4(3x - 1) = 6 - x$

_____ **3.** $2y + 3 = 15 - y$   _____ **8.** $5x + 2 - x = 3 + x + 4x$

_____ **4.** $7y - 1 = 11 + 3y$   _____ **9.** $5 - 3x + 7 = 4x + 3 - 2x$

_____ **5.** $2x - 5 = 7x - 4$   _____ **10.** $3(2 - 5x) + 4 = 3 - 2(x + 1)$

_____ **11.** $|q| + 5 = 11$   _____ **16.** $|6x - 19| = 1$

_____ **12.** $-3 = |z| - 7$   _____ **17.** $|2y + 9| - 4 = 3$

_____ **13.** $|y + 3| = 8$   _____ **18.** $|2y + 9 - 4y| = 3$

_____ **14.** $|5x| = 7$   _____ **19.** $23 = |x + 11|$

_____ **15.** $|2y - 3| = 5$   _____ **20.** $17 = |3x - 1 - x|$

_____ **21.** $\dfrac{4x}{5} = \dfrac{8}{9}$

_____ **22.** $4.3 - 1.4x = -5.5$

_____ **23.** $\dfrac{1}{8} - \dfrac{x}{2} = 4$

_____ **24.** $\dfrac{x}{15} + \dfrac{x}{10} = \dfrac{1}{6}$

_____ **25.** $m + \dfrac{2}{3} = \dfrac{3m}{7}$

_____ **26.** $4.45 + 2.71x = 4.28x - 1.83$

_____ **27.** $\dfrac{x}{28} = \dfrac{3}{8} - \dfrac{5x}{14}$

_____ **28.** $\dfrac{x + 5}{12} = \dfrac{3x - 1}{18}$

_____ **29.** $\dfrac{x + 5}{5} = \dfrac{x}{9} + \dfrac{7}{15}$

_____ **30.** $\dfrac{x + 2}{42} - \dfrac{x}{36} = \dfrac{-5}{252}$

# ■ Practice

## *WORD PROBLEMS*

1. Ninety-seven is five more than four times the number. _____

2. Three consecutive odd numbers add up to 183. Find the numbers.

   _____

3. Ben bought a baseball glove for $5 less than twice the cost of his gym

   bag. If he paid $59 for his glove, how much did he pay for the bag? _____

4. Pete has $165 in five and ten dollar bills. If there are twenty bills total,

   how many of each are there? _____

5. Carrie drives to her mother's house in three hours and returns in four. If
   her speed was 13 mph slower on the return trip, how fast did she drive

   each way? _____

6. A freight train and a passenger train leave Portland at the same time
   heading for Springfield. The passenger train goes 30 mph faster than the
   freight. In six hours the passenger train travels three times farther. What

   is the speed of each train? _____

7. Lisa has nickels, dimes, and quarters totaling $5.50. She has three less
   quarters than dimes, and the number of nickels is one less than twice the
   number of dimes. How many of each coin does she have?

   _____

8. Terry needs 20 gallons of 40% acid. The only available acid solutions are

   25% and 80%. How much of each should she mix?

   _____

9. Stacy has a fruit and nut mix that weighs nine ounces and contains two
   percent pumpkin seeds. How many ounces of pumpkin seeds should she
   add to increase the mix to 7 percent pumpkin seeds?

   _____

10. Ralph is twelve years less than twice as old as Roger. In 8 years the sum
    of their ages will be 109. How old are they now?

    _____

# ■ Cumulative Review

**Identify each type of number.**

_____ **1.** $\sqrt[3]{5}$

_____ **2.** $\sqrt[3]{8}$

_____ **3.** $-5$

_____ **4.** $-\dfrac{3}{5}$

_____ **5.** $0$

**Graph.**

**6.** $-3$

**7.** $\dfrac{5}{3}$

**8.** $\pm 4$

**Evaluate if $a = -3$, $b = -\dfrac{1}{2}$, $c = 4$.**

_____ **9.** $2 - abc$

_____ **10.** $a^0 + b^{-1} + c^2$

**Simplify.**

_____ **11.** $-5 - 8$ _____ **15.** $|0|$

_____ **12.** $(-5x)(-8x)$ _____ **16.** $3^{-5} \div 3^{-2}$

_____ **13.** $\dfrac{3}{20} - \dfrac{5}{24}$ _____ **17.** $2x - 5x + 4 \cdot 3 - 3x - 28$

_____ **14.** $\dfrac{\frac{3}{7}}{9}$ _____ **18.** $-(-\sqrt{25})$

**Translate.**

_____ **19.** Five more than nine times a number

_____ **20.** The perimeter of a rectangle having a length two feet longer than the width

**Solve.**

_____ **21.** $3x = 18$

_____ **22.** $7x - 9 = 26$

_____ **23.** $5x + 3 = 3x - 11$

_____ **24.** $7x - 2(x + 3) = 4$

_____ **25.** $|3x + 2| = 5$

_____ **26.** $\frac{x}{3} + \frac{1}{4} = \frac{5}{6}$

_____ **27.** $ax + b = c$ for $x$

_____ **28.** The sum of two consecutive numbers is 37. Find the numbers.

_____ **29.** Bill drives from Charleston to Forest Hills in 5 hours every Monday, but last Monday it took him six hours. He drove 10 mph slower because of the weather. How fast does Bill usually drive?

_____ **30.** Martha has 19 coins in nickels and dimes. If she has $1.30 total, how many of each coin does she have?

**31.** What property allows you to combine like terms $(5x + 3x)$?

_____

**32.** What property allows you to solve equations of the form $ax = c$?

_____

_____ **33.** Using $Prt = I$, find $I$ if $P = \$30$, $r = 0.08$, and $t = 20$ years.

_____ **34.** Find $\{3, 6, 9, 12, \ldots\} \cap \{2, 4, 6, 8, \ldots\}$.

_____ **35.** Factor 780 into primes.

_____ **36.** Find the LCM of 780 and 1200.

_____ **37.** Find the distance between 7 and $-3$ on the number line.

_____ **38.** Find the midpoint between 7 and $-3$ on the number line.

_____ **39.** Find the average of 9, 12, 13, and 20.

**40.** Write from memory John 3:16. What mathematical principle can you

illustrate from this verse? _____

_____

_____

## Bible: Whole Numbers in Old Testament Prophecy

Find the numbers in each book of prophecy below. Remember that a score is 20. List the numbers together with the units as you did before. Be neat! You will refer back to these. For Lamentations, supply the verse in which you found zero represented by "none." For Malachi, supply the verses that contain the word meaning one-tenth in the Hebrew.

| | Book | Verse | Numbers | Objects/Units |
|---|---|---|---|---|
| 1. | Isaiah | 38:5 | | |
| 2. | Jeremiah | 52:30 | | |
| 3. | Lamentations | | 0 | persons |
| 4. | Ezekiel | 41:12 | | |
| 5. | Daniel | 10:13 | | |
| 6. | Hosea | 6:2 | | |
| 7. | Joel | 2:23 | | |
| 8. | Amos | 2:1 | | |
| 9. | Obadiah | 11 | | |
| 10. | Jonah | 4:11 | | |
| 11. | Micah | 5:5 | | |
| 12. | Nahum | 1:9 | | |
| 13. | Habakkuk | 1:12 | | |
| 14. | Zephaniah | 1:10 | | |
| 15. | Haggai | 2:16 | | |
| 16. | Zechariah | 1:7 | | |
| 17. | Malachi | | $\frac{1}{10}$ | tithes, assets |

18. The only whole number in Malachi is the word "none." Can you find it? (The number one appears in 2:3, but does not translate a Hebrew number.)

_____

19. Review Judges 16:30 as a memory verse. Which kinds of numbers are

being compared? _____

# Math History: Modern Symbols Introduced After 1600

You have already learned that the following symbols were in use by 1600: place value numerations, arabic numerals, fraction bars, plus signs, minus signs, radical signs, equal signs, and grouping symbols.

1. Decimal points first appeared in the English translation of *Descriptio* by John Napier. This book was published the year before his death. What year was this published? (Note: Francesco Pellos used a similar symbol around 1500). _____

   Bombelli's strange grouping symbols (see Chapter 2) were replaced by brackets in *Invention nouvelle l'algebra* by Girard published in 1629.

2. Thomas Harriot wrote *Artis Analyticae Praxis*, but he died ten years before it was printed. The *Praxis* introduced three of our modern symbols: the dot for multiplication and the inequalities $<$ and $>$. What year did Harriot die? _____

3. The same year that Harriot's book was published, William Oughtred published *Clovis mathematicae*. Oughtred introduced the $\times$ for multiplication in his book. What year was this published? _____

4. Rene Descartes introduced a third way of showing multiplication. He simply juxtaposed the factors, putting them side by side. Descartes was also the first to write powers as exponents in *Discours de la method*. However, it was not until 1659 that John Wallis used negative (and fractional) exponents. Give the year of publication for Descartes's book.

   _____

5. The division sign was also developed in 1659, appearing in a work by Johann Heinrich Rahn. Rahn probably combined two symbols for division: 2-3 and 2:3. The colon was used for ratios on the last two pages of *Canones Sinuum*, written by William Oughtred and published in 1657. Do you remember what the other earlier symbol for division meant?

   _____

6. The symbol $\pi$ first appeared in a book by William Jones, published in 1706, and the inequalities $\leq$ and $\geq$ were first used by P. Bouguer in 1734.

   In what years did Bouguer live? _____

# *Calculator Skills*

## MEMORY STORAGE AND RETRIEVAL

How can you find $5 - 3(7.1 - 4.9)$? You already know two methods. Using *parentheses* enables you to enter the numbers in the same order that they are written: 5 $\boxed{-}$ 3 $\boxed{\times}$ $\boxed{(}$ 7.1 $\boxed{-}$ 4.9 $\boxed{)}$ $\boxed{=}$. Try it. Did you get $-1.6$? Using *algebra* you can perform the computations in the order required by the order of operations: 7.1 $\boxed{-}$ 4.9 $\boxed{=}$ $\boxed{\times}$ $- 3$ $\boxed{+}$ 5. This method saves keystrokes and eliminates the need for parentheses, but you must think clearly. Try it. Did you get the same answer?

A third method uses *memory*. The calculator's memory is like scratch paper. It lets you hold a number for later use. Putting a number into the memory is called *storage* and getting it back out is called *retrieval*. When you start a problem that will involve memory, it is necessary to remove from memory numbers previously stored. This is called *clearing* the memory. Here are some common keys that appear on calculators. Look for the ones used by your calculator. If none appear, refer to your manual to determine how your calculator's memory works.

$C$ = clear    $M$ = memory    $R$ = recall (or retrieve)

clear:      $\boxed{\text{MC}}$   $\boxed{\text{CM}}$
storage:    $\boxed{\text{Min}}$  $\boxed{\text{x}{\rightarrow}\text{M}}$   $\boxed{\text{STO}}$
retrieval:  $\boxed{\text{MR}}$   $\boxed{\text{RM}}$   $\boxed{\text{RCL}}$

If your calculator has three memories, you may need to press $\boxed{\text{M}}$ or $\boxed{\text{STO}}$ and then $\boxed{2}$ to tell it to store the number in memory location 2. The same will be true when you recall. Another key that may be used in conjunction with memory is $\boxed{\text{M+}}$. This key allows you to add something to the amount already in storage. If you have trouble clearing your memory you may have a calculator that requires you to press zero and enter that into memory. Check to see if turning off the calculator clears memory. For many calculators this will not be the case. Now do the problem above using memory: $\boxed{\text{MC}}$ 7.1 $-$ 4.9 $\boxed{=}$ $\boxed{\text{Min}}$ 5 $\boxed{-}$ 3 $\boxed{\times}$ $\boxed{\text{MR}}$ $\boxed{=}$.

Look at this problem:

$$11.8 \div [5.7(3.6^2 - 4.2) + 3.2(1.9 - 5.7) + 4.8(3.6^2 - 4.2)]$$

Since there are several sets of parentheses, the algebraic method will not eliminate the need for them. The parentheses method will work, but the memory method is fastest because the quantity $3.6^2 - 4.2$ can be calculated and stored once but recalled without calculating it over again:

3.6 $\boxed{\text{x}^2}$ $\boxed{-}$ 4.2 $\boxed{=}$ $\boxed{\text{Min}}$ $\boxed{\times}$ 5.7 $\boxed{+}$ 3.2 $\boxed{\times}$ $\boxed{(}$ 1.9 $\boxed{-}$ 5.7 $\boxed{)}$ $\boxed{+}$ 4.8 $\boxed{\times}$ $\boxed{\text{MR}}$ $\boxed{=}$ $\boxed{\text{Min}}$ 11.8 $\div$ $\boxed{\text{MR}}$ $\boxed{=}$

Notice that after the bracketed quantity was computed (second $\boxed{=}$ ), it was put in memory (in place of the no longer needed value) and then divided into11.8. Did you get 0.1478?

Identify which method is fastest for each expression below and then find the answer.

1. $2.7 + 5.3\,(11.9)$ _____

2. $2.1\,(3.7 + 6.1) + (3.7 + 6.1)^2$ _____

3. $5.7\,(2.4 - 1.7) - 2.3\,(1.6 + 3.4)$ _____

4. $116^2 - 58\,(23 + 11)^2 + 13\,(47 - 31)$ _____

5. $3\,(92)^2 + 3\,(92) + 17$ _____

6. $97(123 + 51(64 \cdot 23 - 413))$ _____

7. $5136.7\,(3.4) - 5136.7\,(8.9)$ _____

8. $12\,[11.6\,(8.5) - 7.8] + 5.32\,[11.6\,(8.5) - 7.8] - 5$ _____

9. $26\,(5 \cdot 7 + 32) - 5\,(32 \cdot 7 + 111)$ _____

10. $9716\,(9526)^2 + 8403\,(9526 + 9814)$

_____

# Inequalities in Brief: Estimation Skills

Use estimation to decide which quantity is larger. Supply the correct inequality.

_____   **1.** $10.96 \cdot 53.79$         $11.01 \cdot 53.82$

_____   **2.** $16.38 + 14.95$         $3.76 \cdot 7.11$

_____   **3.** $4.21 + 7.25$         $4.21 \cdot 7.25$

_____   **4.** $(7.38)^2$         $(7.38) \cdot (7.35)$

_____   **5.** $92.35 \div 6.21$         $82.14 - 69.74$

_____   **6.** $7.26 + 3.54 \cdot 11.96$         $77.16 \div 10.87 + 43.06$

_____   **7.** $(2.95)^3$         $(2.04)^4$

_____   **8.** $5.92 - 18.42 \div 9.19$         $(10.5)(0.11) + 2.5$

_____   **9.** $195.17 \div 4.91$         $201.78 \div 5.02$

_____   **10.** $517.87 + 396.34$         $839.66 + 99.81$

_____   **11.** $(5.73)^{-1}$         $(5.73)^{-2}$

_____   **12.** $(0.52)^{-1}$         $(0.52)^{-2}$

_____   **13.** $(-7.21)(-4.0)$         $(9.09)(3.88)$

_____   **14.** $(-15.36)(2.13) - 2.55$         $(11.22)(-3.06) - 1.83$

_____   **15.** $(-7.17)^3$         $(-3.02)^5$

_____   **16.** $14.87 \div (-2.94) + 0.96$    $1.11 - (2.49)(3.04)$

_____   **17.** $11.97 - 64.25$         $(7.23)(7.09)$

_____   **18.** $\sqrt{\dfrac{100}{9}}$         $48.13 \div 15.98$

_____   **19.** $\sqrt{\dfrac{100.01}{8.99}}$         $\dfrac{100.01}{\sqrt{8.99}}$

_____   **20.** $\dfrac{\sqrt{100.13}}{8.91}$         $\sqrt{\dfrac{100.13}{8.91}}$

_____   **21.** $(-35.41)(3.22)$         $(-10.46)(-7.59)$

_____   **22.** $11.89 + 7.35 - 2.18$         $9.86 - 1.24 + 8.26$

_____   **23.** $-9.41 \div 2.88 \cdot 3.04$         $3.42 (-3.05) \div 0.97$

_____   **24.** $(-4.27) \div 28.08$         $4.92 \div (-54.78)$

_____   **25.** $43.29 - 40.81$         $57.26 - 60.86$

# Inequalities Applied: World Religions

Obtain an up-to-date world almanac. Find the religion pages in the table of contents and then find the estimated religious population of the world. (You may be able to find this in an encyclopedia, but the almanac should be more up-to-date).

1. What subheadings does the table give for Christians?

   _____

2. Which subgroup is your church classified under? _____

3. Remember that even though many of these subdivisions do not teach people how to be saved, they do recognize the importance of the Bible and Jesus Christ. For each area of the world, divide the total of all "Christians" by the total religious population for that area. Arrange the areas of the world in order from greatest to least chance of hearing about Jesus from the Bible.

   _____

   _____

4. In what area does an individual have the least opportunity to hear? What are the four leading religions in that area?

   _____

5. Repeat question 3 for Protestants instead of all Christians. This group should have the best chance of really knowing how to be saved.

   _____

   _____

6. Where is the biggest need for help? Where could you be of most help for

   telling people how to be saved? _____

7. Can you explain why Latin America is closer to the top of the list in

   question 3 than 5? _____

**8.** Make a bar graph showing the percentages of Protestants by region.

**9.** Divide the total population of North America by the world population.

What percentage of the world lives in North America? _____

**10.** Did you know that over 90% of all Christian workers work in North America? Therefore 90%+ of the workers are trying to minister to _____% of the world. Write an inequality.

_____

# Inequalities in Detail: Absolute Values

You remember that $|x|$ represents the distance between $x$ and zero on the number line.

Draw number lines for $|-5|$ and $|3|$ to show how this works.

**1.** $|-5|$

**2.** $|3|$

Now make number lines for these quantities. Then make a second number line and graph the two quantities being subtracted.

**3.** $|3 - 6|$

**4.** $|8 - 1|$

**5.** $|7 - 11|$

**6.** $|2 - (-3)|$

**7.** The distance between $(3 - 6)$ and zero and the distance between the subtrahends 3 and 6 are related. How are they related? How do your graphs show this?

_____

_____

**8.** This means that you can think of $|a - b|$ in two ways. Name them.

_____

_____

**9.** Write what $|x - 8| \le 12$ means according to the new interpretation.

_____

Write an absolute value inequality with the following graphs.

**10.**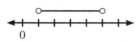

**11.** 

**12.** Look at the graph given below. What is the midpoint of the segment? What is true about the distance from any point on the graph to that

midpoint? _____

**13.** Write an absolute value inequality to represent this relationship.

_____

Write an absolute value inequality with these graphs.

**14.** 

**15.**

# ■ Practice

### PROPERTIES OF INEQUALITIES

**Graph.**

**1.** $x < 3$                **6.** $x > 1$

**2.** $x \geq -4$               **7.** $x \neq \dfrac{7}{2}$

**3.** $x \neq 2$               **8.** $x \leq 30$

**4.** $x > 0$                **9.** $x < -5$

**5.** $x \leq -1$               **10.** $x \geq 2.4$

**Solve.**

_____ **11.** $x + 5 > 9$          _____ **16.** $4x \neq 3$

_____ **12.** $x - 3 < 8$          _____ **17.** $11 + x < 4$

_____ **13.** $5x \leq 100$         _____ **18.** $-2x \leq -4$

_____ **14.** $-3x \geq -6$         _____ **19.** $\dfrac{x}{-5} > 7$

_____ **15.** $\dfrac{x}{2} > -4$        _____ **20.** $x - 3 \neq -4$

**Solve and graph.**

_____ **21.** $x - 6 > 4$

_____ **22.** $3x \leq 18$

_____ **23.** $x + 4 \neq 1$

_____ **24.** $-2x < 14$

_____ **25.** $3 \leq x + 5$

_____ **26.** $\frac{x}{2} \geq -4$

**Identify the inequality property required to solve. Give the solution.**

**27.** $-4x < 8$ _____

**28.** $-4 + x < 8$ _____

**29.** $x + 4 < 8$ _____

**30.** $\frac{x}{4} < 8$ _____

# Practice

## SOLVING INEQUALITIES

**Solve each inequality.**

_____ **1.** $2x + 5 < 3$

_____ **2.** $7 - x \leq 6$

_____ **3.** $3x - 16 > 5$

_____ **4.** $-2x + 41 \geq 23$

_____ **5.** $4 - 5x < 7$

_____ **6.** $3x + 8 \neq 17$

_____ **7.** $14 \leq 2 - 3x$

_____ **8.** $3 > 5 + 6x$

_____ **9.** $\frac{x}{5} - 3 \geq 4$

_____ **10.** $\frac{x}{-2} + 1 < 9$

**Solve each inequality.**

_____ **11.** $3x < x - 6$

_____ **12.** $5 - 2x \geq 4 + x$

_____ **13.** $3x + 7 > 2x - 5$

_____ **14.** $\frac{7 - x}{10} \leq \frac{6}{5}$

_____ **15.** $\frac{2x}{9} + \frac{5}{6} < 3$

_____ **16.** $3x - 4 + x > 5 - 6x + 2$

_____ **17.** $6 + 2(3 + x) \leq 5 + 5x$

_____ **18.** $4(x - 5) \neq 7x$

_____ **19.** $2(3 - x) + x \geq 2x + 1$

_____ **20.** $3x + 5 \neq 4 + 8x + 7 - 4x$

**Solve and graph each inequality.**

_____ **21.** $19 + 4x \neq -1$

_____ **22.** $3 - 4x < 2x$

_____ **23.** $5 + x \geq 3 - x$

_____ **24.** $4 - (3x + 8) \leq 2x + 11$

_____ **25.** $\frac{x-1}{5} > 4 + \frac{x}{2}$

# Practice

### COMPOUND INEQUALITIES

**Solve each compound inequality.**

_____ **1.** $x \leq 3$ and $x > 5$

_____ **2.** $x \geq 4$ or $x > -1$

_____ **3.** $3x < 6$ and $x + 4 \leq 5$

_____ **4.** $-2x \geq 4$ or $x - 7 < 0$

_____ **5.** $|x + 4| < 8$

_____ **6.** $|x| \geq 5$

_____ **7.** $5x + 7 < 6 \vee 3x + 8 \leq 9$

_____ **8.** $|5x + 4| \leq 1$

_____ **9.** $2x - 3 > x + 4 \wedge 5(x + 1) > 18 - x$

_____ **10.** $x \neq 2$ or $x \neq 3$

**Solve and graph each compound inequality.**

_____ **11.** $x \geq 4$ or $x > 4$

_____ **12.** $x \leq -5$ and $x \geq -5$

_____ **13.** $3x > 12$ or $x + 5 < 9$

_____ **14.** $|x| > -2$

_____ **15.** $\frac{x}{5} > 8$ and $x - 3 < 31$

_____ **16.** $|x + 7| > 4$

_____ **17.** $-3x + 5 \geq 14 \wedge 2x \geq -20$

_____ **18.** $5x \leq x + 7 \vee 4x - 1 > 3x + 1$

_____ **19.** $x > -1$ and $x > 1$

_____ **20.** $|2x + 4| > 10$

**Word problems.**

_____ **21.** A number is less than five or less than seven. Find the number.

_____ **22.** Three times a number is more than six and less than fifteen. Find the number.

_____ **23.** The absolute value of a number is less than six. Find the number.

_____ **24.** Seven less than twice a number is at most three or at least five. Find the number.

_____ **25.** Casey has taken three tests and has gotten 78, 96, and 87 points respectively out of 100. What score (out of 100) must he earn on the last test to have an average of at least 90?

# Cumulative Review

**Match.**

_____ 1. $\subseteq$     **A.** conjunction

_____ 2. $<$     **B.** disjunction

_____ 3. $=$     **C.** empty set

_____ 4. $\vee$     **D.** equal

_____ 5. $\cup$     **E.** greater than

_____ 6. $>$     **F.** intersection

_____ 7. $\wedge$     **G.** less than

_____ 8. $\cap$     **H.** element

_____ 9. $\varnothing$     **I.** subset

_____ 10. $\in$     **J.** union

**Identify each property.**

11. $4 < 5$ so $-4 > -5$ _____

12. $4 + 1 = 5$ so $\dfrac{(4 + 1)}{2} = \dfrac{5}{2}$ _____

13. $2(4 + 1)$ is $2 \cdot 4 + 2 \cdot 1$ _____

14. $4 < 5$ so $4 + 3 < 5 + 3$ _____

15. $4 + -4$ is $0$ _____

16. $2^4 \cdot 2^3$ is $2^7$ _____

17. $5 \cdot 3$ is $3 \cdot 5$ _____

18. $4 + 1 = 5$ so $4 + 1 - 3 = 5 - 3$ _____

19. $-5 \cdot 1$ is $-5$ _____

20. $3 + (5 + 8)$ is $(3 + 5) + 8$ _____

**Simplify.**

_____ 21. $2^{31} \cdot 2^{48}$

_____ 22. $|5 \cdot -4|$

_____ 23. $\sqrt[3]{-64}$

_____ 24. $(5 + (3 \cdot -2 + 4) \div 6 \cdot 3) \div 2$

_____ **25.** $(5^{-1} x^2)^{-2}$

_____ **26.** $4x + 3y - 2x + 5y + xy$

**Evaluate using** $x = 2, y = -3, z = -1.$

_____ **27.** $x^2 y z^2 + x - z$        _____ **28.** $2x^0 \div (y + z)$

**Solve.**

_____ **29.** $3x + 5 = 2x + 1$

_____ **30.** $x + 8 < 5$

_____ **31.** $\frac{4}{5}x - \frac{1}{15} = \frac{1}{10}$

_____ **32.** $4 - 3x \leq 16$

_____ **33.** $|2x - 7| > 1$

_____ **34.** $4x + 1 \neq 3$ and $2x - 5 \geq -6$

**Word Problems.**

**35.** Five more than three times a number is six. Find the number.

_____

**36.** Three less than six times a number is at least fifteen less than four times

the number. Find the number. _____

**37.** Two blimps leave Wilmington in opposite directions and are thirty miles
apart after two hours. If one travels five mph faster than the other, how

fast is each? _____

**38.** Patsy has five more dimes than quarters and the combined value is at
least three dollars. What is the minimum number of quarters that Patsy

has? _____

**39.** Faith Christian Academy had a family fair. The admission price was only
a quarter for adults and a dime for students. They sold ten more
children's tickets than adults, and they received at least thirty dollars in
tickets. What is the minimum number of adult tickets sold?

_____

**40.** Write out Luke 15:4.

_____

_____

_____

# CHAPTER 6
## Relations, Functions, and Graphs

## Bible: Whole Numbers in the Old Testament

Find natural numbers between four and 110 in each of the five poetical books of the Old Testament. This will complete the finding of numbers in every book of the Old Testament.

| Book | Verse | Numbers | Object/Unit |
|---|---|---|---|
| Job | 1:2 | | sons, daughters |
| Psalms | 90:10 | | years (age) |
| Proverbs | 9:1 | | pillars |
| Ecclesiastes | 6:3 | | children |
| Song of Solomon | 6:8 | | queens; concubines |

You have found all the following numbers in the Old Testament. Complete the list below by giving the reference containing each whole number.

| | | |
|---|---|---|
| 0. | 11. | 21. |
| 1. | 12. | 22. |
| 2. | 13. | 23. |
| 3. | 14. | 24. |
| 4. | 15. | 25. |
| 5. | 16. | 26. |
| 6. | 17. | 27. |
| 7. | 18. | 28. |
| 8. | 19. | 29. |
| 9. | 20. | 30. |
| 10. | | |

Now see if you can continue your list up through 42. Genesis 11:12-20, II Kings 15:8-13, and I Chronicles 29:27 provide several of them. Use a concordance to find the others, but be careful not to use a verse for 36 that is actually talking about 136.

| | | |
|---|---|---|
| 31. | 35. | 39. |
| 32. | 36. | 40. |
| 33. | 37. | 41. |
| 34. | 38. | 42. |

**43.** Review Numbers 23:19 as a memory verse. What does this Old Testament verse tell you about all these numbers? How do the statements that have numbers in them relate to reality? _____

## Math History: Eudoxus

1. When did Eudoxus live? _____

2. Where was Eudoxus from? _____

3. Name the place where he moved in order to study with the Pythagoreans.

   _____

4. Where did he travel with Plato? _____

5. Where did he found a school? _____

6. Where did he later go to teach? _____

Since none of the writings of Eudoxus have survived, all that we know of him is based on what other ancient writings record about him. Archimedes acknowledged that important principles of proportions and surface areas had been discovered by Eudoxus. Procius recorded that Eudoxus had studied the golden ratio.

7. What ancient geometer used definitions and proofs first given by

   Eudoxus? _____

8. Eudoxus laid the proper basis for proportions. What type of proportions did you study in this chapter?

   _____

9. Although Eudoxus advanced the study of proportions and of areas, what erroneous views of astronomy did he hold?

   _____

# *Calculator Skills*

### FACTORIALS

The symbol 4! is read "four factorial" and means that you must multiply all the natural numbers up to 4 together: 4! means $4 \cdot 3 \cdot 2 \cdot 1$, or 24. Do you see that 7! would mean $7 \cdot 6 \cdot 5 \cdot 4 \cdot 3 \cdot 2 \cdot 1$, or 5040?

Find the $\boxed{x!}$ key on your calculator. This will be a 2nd function key on most calculators and will require $\boxed{\text{2nd}}$ or $\boxed{\text{shift}}$ in conjunction with the $\boxed{x!}$. Press $\boxed{4}$, $\boxed{\text{2nd}}$, $\boxed{x!}$. Did you get 24? Now use your calculator to verify that 7! = 5040.

One application of factorials involves the multiplication principle of counting. How many ways can you arrange 4 books on a shelf? There are four choices for the first book and 3 choices left for the second book and 2 choices for the third book and finally one choice for the last book. The word *and* reminds us to use the multiplication principle $4 \cdot 3 \cdot 2 \cdot 1$, which is 4! The number of ways to arrange *n* objects is *n*!.

How many ways can you arrange 50 books on a shelf?

$50! = 50 \cdot 49 \cdot 48 \cdot \ldots \cdot 3 \cdot 2 \cdot 1$. This is a very large number, so using your calculator saves a lot of time. Find 50! on your calculator. Do you remember that the answer is in scientific notation, and the 64 is the power of ten? $50! = 3.0414 \times 10^{64}$. Are you glad you didn't have to multiply all 50 numbers together to get the 65-digit answer?

Can you guess what 0! should be? Since factorials mean consecutive multiplications, you should guess that they will be similar to exponents, which are repeated multiplications. In both cases the answer is the identity element for multiplication: $5^0 = 1$ and $0! = 1$. Check this on your calculator.

### Practice.

1. How many ways can you arrange 8 books on a shelf? _____

2. How many different ways can you line up a class of 11 students?

   _____

3. Find 20! and 60! _____

4. What is the largest factorial that your calculator can compute?

   _____

5. Find $\frac{12!}{4!}$, $\frac{12!}{4}$, $\frac{12}{4!}$, and $\left(\frac{12}{4}\right)!$. _____

_____  **6.** Find $8! - 5!$ and $(8 - 5)!$. Are they equal?

_____  **7.** Find $7!2!$ and $(7 \cdot 2)!$. Are they equal?

_____  **8.** Find $(3^2)!$ and $(3!)^2$. Are they equal?

_____  **9.** Find $\frac{16!}{7!}$.

_____  **10.** Find $\frac{16!}{7!9!}$.

# Estimation in Brief: Solutions of Inequalities

Decide which of the choices is a solution by using estimates in your check of the possible answers given.

_____  **1.** $|4.7x - 3.8| \leq 1.7$

  **a.** 2.3   **b.** 1.5   **c.** 1.1   **d.** $-0.5$

_____  **2.** $3.2x + 1.1 > 4.3$

  **a.** 1.0   **b.** 0.6   **c.** $-3.4$   **d.** none of the above

_____  **3.** $-1.3x + 2.4 < 2.1$

  **a.** $-1.4$   **b.** 0   **c.** 0.7   **d.** none of the above

_____  **4.** $\dfrac{x - 4.9}{5.1} \geq 2.9$

  **a.** 5.4   **b.** 25.7   **c.** $-11.6$   **d.** 16.4

_____  **5.** $3.2 - 4.6x \leq 1.8$

  **a.** 0.9   **b.** $-0.5$   **c.** $-1.6$   **d.** $-4.2$

Now estimate the solution set of the inequality by selecting the best answer.

_____  **6.** $4.9x + 4.2 > 6.1$

  **a.** $x > 2$   **b.** $x > \frac{2}{5}$   **c.** $x > \frac{1}{2}$   **d.** $x > \frac{5}{2}$

_____  **7.** $7.3 - 2.7x \leq 4.2$

  **a.** $x \geq 1$   **b.** $x \leq -1$   **c.** $x \geq -1$   **d.** $x \leq 1$

_____  **8.** $9.6 - 1.1x < 2.8 + 4.2x$

  **a.** $x < 1.3$   **b.** $x < 2.1$   **c.** $x > 1.3$   **d.** $x > 2.1$

_____  **9.** $\dfrac{2.05x + 18.17}{3.26} \geq 1.91$

  **a.** $x \geq -6$   **b.** $x \geq 12$   **c.** $x \geq -9$   **d.** $x \geq 9$

_____  **10.** $-2.4x \geq 9.7$

  **a.** $x \geq -3$   **b.** $x \geq -5$   **c.** $x \leq -3$   **d.** $x \leq -5$

# Graphing Applied: Revenue and Profit

As the president of the company, you keep tabs on new products. The production manager brings the following graphs pertaining to your latest men's watch.

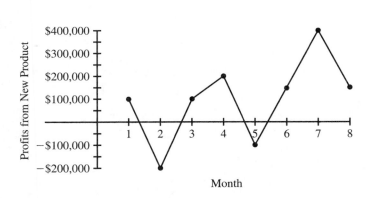

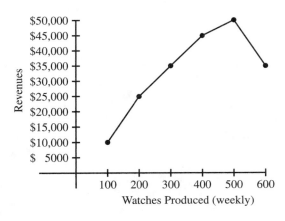

Production began in January of this year. It is now September. Profits are shown monthly through August.

_____  **1.** In which months did the company lose money?

_____  **2.** In which month did they experience their greatest profit? How much profit was earned?

_____  **3.** Which month showed the greatest loss? How much was the loss?

_____  **4.** For the entire eight months, how much money has been gained (or lost)?

_____  **5.** Is the overall trend encouraging? Would you expect next month's profits to go up or down?

The second graph shows how much income was received based on various production schedules over several weeks. Producing more and more watches does not mean more and more profit. If the watches must be cleared at reduced rates or do not sell at all, more watches could reduce profit. Use the second graph to answer these questions.

**6.** What is the revenue from 300 watches? What is the average selling price per watch? _____

**7.** How many watches do they produce to create enough demand to sell them at the highest rate? _____

**8.** How many watches should be produced to generate the most revenue (income)? _____

9. Marginal revenue is the slope of the line. Which marginal revenue is greatest (shows greatest increase of revenue)? _____

10. In August, 500 watches were produced each of the four weeks. Find the revenues, profits, and costs ($P = R - C$). _____

# Graphing in Detail: Parallel and Perpendicular Lines

1. Graph the lines $y = 3x + 2$ and $y = 3x - 5$ on the same graph.

2. What do you notice about these lines? _____

3. Now graph the lines $y = 3x + 2$ and $y = -\frac{1}{3}x + 4$ on a second graph.

4. What do you notice about these lines? _____

5. Graph the lines $y = -\frac{2}{3}x + 5$ and $y = \frac{3}{2}x$ on another graph.

6. What do you notice about these lines? _____

Using the graphs you just made, draw conclusions about the following.

_____ **7.** What is the relationship of the signs of the slopes of parallel lines?

_____ **8.** What is the relationship of the signs of the slopes of perpendicular lines?

_____ **9.** What is true of the absolute values of the slopes of parallel lines?

_____ **10.** What is true of the absolute values of the slopes of perpendicular lines?

**Give the slope of a line parallel to a line having a slope of**

_____ **11.** $\frac{2}{7}$

_____ **12.** $-5$

**Give the slope of a line perpendicular to a line having a slope of**

_____ **13.** $6$

_____ **14.** $\frac{2}{7}$

_____ **15.** $-3$

_____ **16.** $-\frac{1}{5}$

**17.** Give the equation of a line perpendicular to $y = 3x + 7$ with the same

$y$-intercept. _____

**18.** Give the equation of a line perpendicular to $y = -\frac{3}{4}x + 4$ that passes

through $(3, 5)$. _____

# ■ Practice

## POINTS AND RELATIONS

**Graph each point.**

**1.** $(-3, 5)$                    **6.** $(-6, -1)$

**2.** $(0, 4)$                      **7.** $(4, 0)$

**3.** $(2, -8)$                     **8.** $(0, -2)$

**4.** $(1, 3)$                      **9.** $(-3, -4)$

**5.** $(0, 0)$                      **10.** $(-2, 0)$

**Identify each point on the graph.**

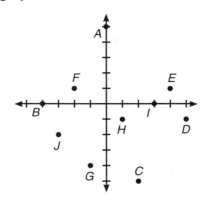

_____ **11.** A        _____ **16.** F

_____ **12.** B        _____ **17.** G

_____ **13.** C        _____ **18.** H

_____ **14.** D        _____ **19.** I

_____ **15.** E        _____ **20.** J

**Are these relations functions?**

_____ **21.** $\{(4, 1), (2, 3), (-3, 0)\}$

_____ **22.** $\{(3, -1), (5, -1)\}$

_____ **23.** $\{(4, 2), (4, -3)\}$

_____ **24.**

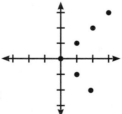

_____ **25.**

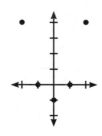

© 2000 BJU Press. Reproduction prohibited.

**Graph each relation.**

26. $\{(x, y)\,|\,y = -4x, x = -2, -1, 0, 1\}$

27. $\{(x, y)\,|\,y = |x - 4|, x = 2, 4, 6\}$

28. $\{(x, y)\,|\,x = y^2, x = 0, 4\}$

29. $\{(x, y)\,|\,y = x^3 - 4x, x = -1, 0, 2\}$

30. $\{(x, y)\,|\,0 < x \leq 3, 0 < y < 3, x\,\&\,y\text{ are integers}\}$

# ■ Practice

## GRAPHS OF LINES

**Graph each line by plotting points. Label each *y*-intercept.**

**1.** $4x = y$

**3.** $y = 4x - 2$

**2.** $3x + y = 7$

**4.** $5x - 4y = 12$

**Give the slope of each graph and its *y*-intercept.**

_____ **5.**

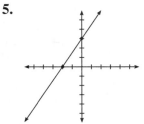

_____ **7.**

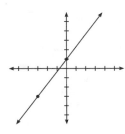

_____ **6.**

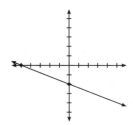

_____ **8.**

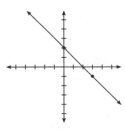

**Given the two points, find the slope.**

_____ **9.** $(0, 7), (3, 2)$

_____ **10.** $(-5, 3), (2, 1)$

_____ **11.** $(-1, -4), (-3, 6)$

_____ **12.** $(4, -1), (6, 3)$

_____ **13.** $(9, 6), (-3, 0)$

_____ **14.** $(8, 4), (3, -2)$

**For each equation, change to slope-intercept form. Identify the slope and *y*-intercept.**

**15.** $y = 4x$ _____

**16.** $y + 8 = 3x$ _____

**17.** $y - 5x = 7$ _____

**18.** $x + 3y = 9$ _____

**19.** $3x + 2y = 9$ _____

**20.** $4x - 7y = 11$ _____

**Use the slope and *y*-intercept to graph each equation.**

**21.** $y = 3x$                    **23.** $y = -2x + 1$

**22.** $y = -4$                    **24.** $y = 2x - 3$

**25.** $x = 5$

**28.** $x + 2y = 4$

**26.** $2x + y = 5$

**29.** $12x - 4y = 8$

**27.** $4x - y = 7$

**30.** $7x + 3y = 15$

# ■ Practice ·····

### LINEAR EQUATIONS AND INEQUALITIES

**Find the equation of each line given the slope and *y*-intercept.**

_____  **1.** $m = 4, b = 2$

_____  **2.** $m = 0, b = 0$

_____  **3.** $m = -3, b = 0$

_____  **4.** $m = 0, b = -3$

_____  **5.** $m = -3, b = -3$

_____  **6.** $m = \frac{2}{3}, b = 1$

_____  **7.** $m = -\frac{1}{4}, b = 3$

_____  **8.** $m = -5, b = \frac{1}{3}$

_____  **9.** $m = \frac{9}{5}, b = 3$

_____  **10.** $m = \frac{2}{9}, b = \frac{5}{6}$

**Find the equation of each line given the slope and one point.
Answer in standard form.**

**11.** $m = 20, (3, 2)$ _____

**12.** $m = \frac{2}{3}, (0, 5)$ _____

**13.** $m = -3, (-2, 1)$ _____

**14.** $m = 0, (6, -7)$ _____

**15.** $m = -\frac{11}{4}, (9, 4)$ _____

**Find the equation of the line given two points. Answer in slope-intercept form.**

_____  **16.** $(2, 3), (4, -1)$

_____  **17.** $(11, -7), (0, -6)$

_____  **18.** $(-3, 11), (2, -4)$

_____  **19.** $(5, 0), (8, 3)$

_____  **20.** $(2, 14), (-3, 15)$

**If *y* varies directly with *x*,**

_____ **21.** find $k$, if $y = 10$ when $x = 2$.

_____ **22.** find $k$, if $y = 3$ when $x = 5$.

_____ **23.** find $y$, if $k = 4$ and $x = \frac{3}{2}$.

_____ **24.** find $y$ when $x = 12$, if $y = 7$ when $x = 4$.

_____ **25.** find $y$ when $x = 6$, if $y = 4$ when $x = 8$.

**Graph each linear inequality on the Cartesian plane.**

**26.** $y > 5x$                        **29.** $2x + y < 7$

**27.** $x \leq -2$                   **30.** $5x - 3y \leq 6$

**28.** $y \geq \frac{11}{3}x - 7$

# ■ Cumulative Review

**Graph $x = 2$ on the**

    **1.** number line.

    **2.** Cartesian plane.

**Using the formula $p = qx^2 + cn$,**

  _____   **3.** find $p$ if $q = -3$, $x = 2$, $c = 8$, and $n = 1$.

  _____   **4.** solve for $c$.

**Is (5, 3) a solution to each of the following?**

  _____   **5.** $2y - 7 = x$

  _____   **6.** $3(x - 4) + 3y = x(x - 3)$

  _____   **7.** $3x - 5y < -2$

  _____   **8.** $2x - y \geq 7$

**Give the equation of the line passing through**

  _____   **9.** (3, 5) with a slope of $-\frac{2}{3}$.

  _____   **10.** (2, 4) and (−3, 1).

**Simplify.**

  _____   **11.** $-6 \cdot 3 + 4 \cdot 2$

  _____   **12.** $\frac{2}{3} \cdot \frac{12}{5} - \frac{8}{9} \div \frac{16}{15} + \frac{9}{100} \cdot \frac{10}{3}$

  _____   **13.** $12x^2 - 5x + 7x^3 - 4x^4 - 12x^2 + x^3 - x^4$

  _____   **14.** $5(xy - x) + 3y(x - 2) + 4(7x - 2y)$

  _____   **15.** $\frac{5^{-1}x^2y^{-1}}{3^{-2}xy^3}$

**Solve.**

_____  **16.** $2(x + 6) = 7$

_____  **17.** $\frac{5}{3} + 2x = \frac{1}{4}$

_____  **18.** $x + 9 < 3$

_____  **19.** $3x - 4 = x + 4$

_____  **20.** $|x - 2| \geq 1$

**Graph on a number line or Cartesian plane as appropriate.**

**21.** $\frac{2}{3}$

**22.** $x = \pm 5$

**23.** $|x - 2| < 4$

**24.** $\{-1, 3, 7\}$

**25.** $\{(x, y) | y = 3, x = 2, 3, 4\}$

**26.** $|5x - 4| = 1$

**27.** $7x + 2 = 5$

**28.** $3x - 1 \geq 4$ or $5x - 1 < 3$

**29.** $x + y = 2$

**30.** $y < 3x - 1$

_____ **31.** What kind of number is 4.72?

_____ **32.** Find $\sqrt{81}$.

_____ **33.** Find $5^{11} \cdot 5^7$.

_____ **34.** Translate into symbols:
Seven less than five times a number.

_____ **35.** Find the slope of the line connecting (6, 3) and (2, −5).

_____ **36.** Find x < −4 and x > −2.

_____ **37.** One number is two more than 3 times another number. If the sum is fifty, find the numbers.

_____ **38.** A certain map shows a scale on which one inch represents two hundred miles. Since the actual distance varies directly with the distance measured on the map, how many inches represent 1150 miles?

_____  **39.** Twenty-four less than four times a number is at
                           least eighty. Find the number.

**40.** Write from memory:
    **a.** Romans 3:10  **b.** John 3:16  **c.** Luke 15:4  **d.** Judges 16:30
    **e.** Numbers 23:19

    **a.** _____
        _____

    **b.** _____
        _____
        _____

    **c.** _____
        _____
        _____
        _____

    **d.** _____
        _____
        _____
        _____
        _____

    **e.** _____
        _____
        _____
        _____

# CHAPTER 7
## Systems of Equations and Inequalities

## Bible: Whole Numbers in the New Testament

Find the numbers in each book of the New Testament. Complete the chart below by using a concordance to find a reference containing the number. Supply units for each number and be neat for later reference as usual.

You can find 5 of these by checking "eight" and "eighth" in a concordance. Another 4 can be found under "first." The hardest are in Luke and I Timothy; remember that a *score* is twenty.

| Book | Verse | Numbers | Objects/Units |
|------|-------|---------|---------------|
| 1. Matthew | | 40 | |
| 2. Mark | | 11 | |
| 3. Luke | | 84 | |
| 4. John | | 38 | |
| 5. Acts | | 8 | |
| 6. Romans | | 7000 | |
| 7. I Corinthians | | 12 | |
| 8. II Corinthians | | 2, 3 | |
| 9. Galatians | | 14 | |
| 10. Ephesians | | 2, 1 | |
| 11. Philippians | | 8 | |
| 12. Colossians | | 1 | |
| 13. I Thessalonians | | 1 | |
| 14. II Thessalonians | | 1 | |
| 15. I Timothy | | 60 | |
| 16. II Timothy | | 1 | |
| 17. Titus | | 1, 2 | |
| 18. Philemon | | 1 | |
| 19. Hebrews | | 7 | |
| 20. James | | 12 | |
| 21. I Peter | | 8 | |
| 22. II Peter | | 8 | |
| 23. I John | | 3 | |
| 24. II John | | 1 | |
| 25. III John | | 0 | |
| 26. Jude | | 7, 10,000 | |
| 27. Revelation | | 24 | |

**28.** What seems to be the most common number in the New Testament? ____

**29.** Review II Corinthians 5:21. What comparison can you make to a principle of numbers based on this verse? Explain.

_____

_____

_____

## Math History: Copernicus

Nicholas Copernicus was an astronomer and mathematician.

1. When did he live? _____

2. Where was he from? _____

3. What was his most famous book? _____

   _____

4. When was the book published? _____

5. What did this book convince the world of? _____

6. Copernicus used a branch of mathematics called trigonometry. This branch of mathematics involves many computations and equations. What did Copernicus use all these computational methods for?

   _____

7. There is one theorem in mathematics that Copernicus is known for. What is the subject of the theorem?

   _____

Copernicus was not the first to make the discovery in question 5. An ancient Greek mathematician and astronomer Aristarchus of Samos also wrote of this, but his conclusions were not accepted.

8. When did Aristarchus live? _____

9. How do we know that he wrote about the same thing as Copernicus?

   _____

10. How long before Copernicus's birth was Aristarchus born? _____

11. What book by Aristarchus can still be read?

    _____

12. The motions of the planets around the sun are described by equations. Studying the relation between Earth and Mars involves the system of equations formed by using the equations for the orbits of Earth and Mars.

    Is this system linear or nonlinear? _____

# Calculator Skills

## MEMORY OPERATIONS

| Revenues | Costs |
|---|---|
| $110.46 | $ 18.96 |
| 97.31 | 100.15 |
| 82.73 | 42.90 |
| 296.25 | 73.15 |
| 153.18 | 81.62 |

Profit is revenue minus cost ($P = R - C$). In Chapter 5 you learned how to use your calculator's memory. To calculate profit, find the total revenue and store it. Then find the total cost, subtract the revenue (memory recall) from the total cost, and change the sign +/−. In this lesson you will learn an alternative method.

Find the M+ key. This button adds the displayed value to the value currently in memory. Enter the following: 110.46 Min 97.31 M+ 82.73 M+ 296.25 M+ 153.18 M+. You will notice that no calculations show on the display but only the numbers being entered. The additions are done directly in the memory. Do you think it worked? Press memory recall; the value in memory is the total 739.93, not the most recent value added. Now add the cost column on the display; do not do anything to the memory. Did you get 316.78? At this point you could subtract and change signs, but you can also do the subtraction in the correct order quite easily. Look for the Display/Memory swap key X↔M; be sure it has arrows on both ends. This key is a second function on many calculators, but some calculators do not have it (in that case, just subtract and change signs). Press the key (hit 2nd first if it is a second function). Notice that the total revenue that was in memory appeared. Now press −, MR, =. When you press memory recall, the total costs reappeared. When the revenues came to the display, the costs were put in memory. This is why the swap key has two arrows; it swaps

the values. What was the total profit? _____

Practice using the M+ and X↔M keys by repeating the above process to find the total profits below.

| | 1. R | C | 2. R | C | 3. R | C | 4. R | C | 5. R | C |
|---|---|---|---|---|---|---|---|---|---|---|
| | $301.11 | $67.24 | $56.60 | $12.10 | $724.37 | $264.72 | $95.10 | $40.07 | $45,367.22 | $ 8952.75 |
| | 198.26 | 83.42 | 43.57 | 15.26 | 851.52 | 341.93 | 93.46 | 30.26 | 37,459.28 | 10,501.06 |
| | 256.77 | 49.56 | 83.44 | 90.42 | 624.91 | 176.26 | 97.35 | 35.53 | 39,508.73 | 11,416.35 |
| | 395.61 | 74.38 | 39.73 | 15.59 | 937.48 | 245.12 | 96.42 | 46.19 | 42,725.64 | 14,058.92 |
| | 227.95 | 51.30 | | | 783.29 | 309.42 | 93.17 | 53.27 | | |
| | 170.06 | 49.99 | | | | | 91.19 | 98.06 | | |

# Systems in Brief: Breaking Even

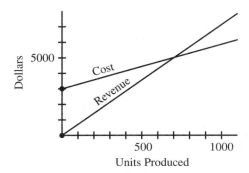

Look at the graph of the *costs* above.

1. Give the equation of the cost line. _____

2. How much does it cost to produce 560 units? _____

3. How many units are produced for $7000? _____

There is some cost to the company even when they produce nothing. These costs are *fixed costs* and include items such as rent for the building.

4. Name other fees that would be included in fixed costs.

_____

5. How much are the fixed costs for this company? _____

6. What is the slope of the cost line? _____

7. Give the marginal cost as a decimal. Include units. _____

Now look at the graph of the *revenues* above.

8. Give the equation of the revenue line. _____

9. How much income results from producing 210 units? _____

10. How many units are produced to generate $3000 revenue? ____

11. Give the slope of the line. _____

12. What does the marginal revenue represent? _____

_____

13. Identify marginal revenue as a decimal. Include units. _____

The system of equations represented by the revenue and cost lines is very important. The solution to this system is called the *break-even point.*

14. Find the break-even point from the graph. _____

**15.** Give an equation for profit by subtracting the equation in question 1 from the equation in question 8.

   Be sure to simplify. _____

**16.** How much profit is there at the break-even point? _____

**17.** What happens if you produce fewer units than break-even?

   _____

**18.** What happens if you produce more than the break-even point?

   _____

# Systems Applied: Ticket Sales

Farmington Christian School recently hosted a symphony orchestra. The orchestra offered to play free as a benefit, but the school spent $5473 renting the city auditorium, advertising, and printing tickets.

The school printed 800 (yellow) children's tickets and 700 (blue) adult tickets. Two tables were set up for sales. The children's tickets sold for $5 each, but a $1 discount applied to the yellow tickets for students of the school. Adult tickets sold for $10 each, but parents of students received a $2 discount on their blue tickets.

The school made $2746 beyond their costs, so it was a very successful venture. The bookkeeper needs to have a record of how many student, other child, parent, and other adult tickets were sold, but nobody kept track of it.

You decide to help out the bookkeeper. You ask the workers from the two ticket tables how many tickets are left. There are 112 yellow tickets and 183 blue tickets left. You also ask how much money was received at each table. The adult sales table received $4932. The children's ticket sales are not available because the funds were combined with jogathon monies and deposited. This doesn't bother you, though, because you know you have enough information to solve your problem. How many tickets were sold at each of the four ticket prices? Make a table to help you write the system of equations needed to solve the problem.

# Systems in Detail: Nonlinear Systems

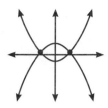

Do you remember using substitution to solve systems that were not linear? Such systems would be graphed using curves and can result in any specific number of solutions. The graph to the right shows a system with two solutions:

**1.** Identify the number of solutions in each graph.

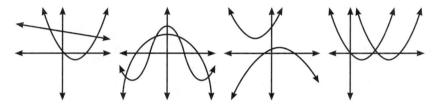

**2.** Can you make a graphical system with 3 solutions?

Another type of system that cannot be graphed using lines occurs when there are more than two unknowns and equations. The addition method will help you solve these.

Example 1. Solve

$$2x + y + z = 8$$
$$x - y + z = 6$$
$$3x + 2y + z = 15$$

Solution. You are trying to find an ordered triple $(x, y, z)$ that will make all three equations true. To solve this system, choose a variable to eliminate by the addition method. Since $z$ has the same coefficient in each equation, it is the easiest to eliminate.

$$\begin{array}{r} 2x + y + z = 8 \\ - \underline{x - y + z = 6} \\ x + 2y \quad\;\; = 2 \end{array}$$

**1.** Subtract to eliminate the $z$ terms in the first and second equations.

$$\begin{array}{r} x - y + z = \;\;6 \\ - \underline{3x + 2y + z = \;15} \\ -2x - 3y \quad\;\; = -9 \end{array}$$

**2.** Next eliminate the $z$ terms in the second and third equations.

$$\begin{array}{r} 2x + 4y = \;\;\;4 \\ + \underline{-2x - 3y = -9} \\ y = -5 \end{array}$$

**3.** Now you have two equations with two unknowns. Solve them as a system. Multiply the first by two and add the equations.

$$x + 2y = 2$$
$$x + 2(-5) = 2$$
$$x - 10 = 2$$
$$x = 12$$

**4.** Substitute $y = -5$ into one of these equations to find $x$.

$$x - y + z = 6$$
$$12 - (-5) + z = 6$$
$$12 + 5 + z = 6$$
$$17 + z = 6$$
$$z = -11$$

**5.** Substitute $x = 12$ and $y = -5$ into one of the original equations.

So the ordered triple that will make all three equations true is $(12, -5, -11)$.

### SOLVING A SYSTEM IN THREE UNKNOWNS

1. Use one or two steps to eliminate one variable and obtain a system of two equations with the same two unknowns.
2. Solve the resulting system.
3. Substitute results in one of the original equations to find the third unknown.

**Solve each system of equations.**

**1.** $2x + y + z = 8$
 $x + y - z = 4$
 $x + z = 6$

**6.** $x - 2y + 3z = 20$
 $3x + 4y - z = -20$
 $x + y - 7z = -53$

**2.** $x + z = 0$
 $y = 3x - 6$
 $x + y + z = 9$

**7.** $x - 3y + 5z = 33$
 $2x - y + 4z = 32$
 $x - 2y - z = -17$

**3.** $x - y = 4$
 $y - z = 8$
 $x + z = 12$

**8.** $3x + y - z = 16$
 $x + y + 2z = 12$
 $x - y + z = 8$

**4.** $2x + y - z = 12$
 $x - y + z = -3$
 $x + y + 3z = 17$

**9.** $x + y = 8$
 $x + z = 2$
 $y + z = 11$

**5.** $3x - y + 2z = -5$
 $x + y + 4z = -3$
 $8x + 2y - z = 18$

**10.** The sum of the digits of a certain three-digit number is 12. The units digit is one more than the hundreds digit. If the tens digit is four more than the units digit, what is the number? _____

# ■ Practice  ·····································································

## GRAPHING SYSTEMS

**Graph each system and solve.**

**1.** $y = 2x - 1$
$y = 5$

**2.** $y = 3x - 1$
$y = -x + 15$

**3.** $y = 4x - 3$
$y = x + 3$

**4.** $x - 2y = 1$
$2x + y = 7$

**5.** $x + y = 3$
$x - y = 11$

**6.** $x + 2y = 3$
$2x + y = -3$

**7.** $3x + y = 1$
$y = -x + 3$

**8.** $4x - 2y = 10$
$6x - 3y = 15$

**9.** $-x + y = 2$
$x - 3y = 0$

**10.** $3x - 2y = 6$
$y = \frac{3}{2}x - 1$

**Solve by graphing and decide whether each system is inconsistent, consistent and independent, or consistent and dependent.**

**11.** $y = 4x + 5$
$y = 2x + 3$

**15.** $5x + 2y = -4$
$2x + 4y = 8$

**12.** $2x + y = 4$
$4x + 2y = 7$

**16.** $x + 2 = 2y$
$3x - 6y = -6$

**13.** $3x + y = 5$
$2x - y = 0$

**17.** $8x - 2y = 4$
$12x - 3y = 9$

**14.** $x + 2y = 6$
$2x + 4y = 12$

**18.** $x - 2y = 4$
$2y - x = 6$

**19.** $3x + y = 4$
$2y - x = 8$

**20.** $4x + 3y = 6$
$2y + 13 = 3x$

**Decide whether these are consistent, inconsistent, dependent, or independent without graphing (use slopes and *y*-intercepts).**

_____ **21.** $5x + 3y = 8$
$2x - 4y = 7$

_____ **22.** $3x + 2y = 6$
$9x + 6y = 4$

_____ **23.** $6x - 4y = 8$
$-3x + 2y = -4$

_____ **24.** $7x - 3y = 2$
$9x + 4y = 6$

_____ **25.** $4x + 2y = 3$
$6x + 3y = 4$

# ■ Practice ···········································································································

### SUBSTITUTION

For each system below, which variable should you replace by substituting an equivalent expression? If they are equally easy, write "either."

_____ **1.** $3x + y = 7$
$2x + 5y = 9$

_____ **6.** $x - 5y = 3$
$3x + 2y = 4$

_____ **2.** $4x - 7y = 3$
$2x + 6y = 10$

_____ **7.** $9x + 3y = 12$
$5x + 4y = -7$

_____ **3.** $2x + 3y = 6$
$5x - y = 3$

_____ **8.** $x + 4y = 6$
$3x - y = 5$

_____ **4.** $7x + 4y = 8$
$5x + 3y = 11$

_____ **9.** $5x + 5y = 15$
$x + 2y = 3$

_____ **5.** $3x + 8y = 5$
$7x - 2y = 9$

_____ **10.** $8x - 2y = 12$
$6x + 18y = 6$

For each system below, find the variable to be replaced and then give the expression to substitute in its place.

_____ **11.** $3x - 7y = 9$
$4x - y = 6$

_____ **15.** $6x + 2y = 8$
$5x - 9y = 11$

_____ **12.** $x + 6y = 4$
$3x - 5y = 7$

_____ **16.** $7x + 5y = 6$
$8x - 4y = 12$

_____ **13.** $7x + y = 9$
$5x - 3y = 7$

_____ **17.** $8x + 9y = 4$
$3x - 6y = 6$

_____ **14.** $5x - 2y = 4$
$x + 3y = 6$

_____ **18.** $3x - 33y = 9$
$4x - 7y = 5$

Solve each system below by substitution.

_____ **19.** $x - y = 7$
$3x - 8y = 11$

_____ **20.** $2x + 5y = 13$
$x + 2y = 5$

_____ **21.** $4x + 3y = 3$
$2x + y = 3$

_____ **22.** $5x - 2y = 15$
$3x + 5y = -22$

_____ **23.** $6x - 7y = -5$
$2x + 3y = 9$

_____ **24.** $4x - 5y = 8$
$7x + 3y = 9$

_____ **25.** $2x + y = 8$
$x + y = 3$

# ■ Practice

## ADDITION METHOD

**For each problem below, which variable should be eliminated first? Which equations must be multiplied?**

_____  1. $x + y = 7$
$\qquad\;\; 2x - y = 8$

_____  2. $2x + 3y = 6$
$\qquad\;\; 3x + y = 5$

_____  3. $x - 3y = 8$
$\qquad\;\; 5x + 4y = 11$

_____  4. $3x + 2y = 7$
$\qquad\;\; 11x - 6y = 4$

_____  5. $8x + 3y = 17$
$\qquad\;\; 4x + 5y = 3$

_____  6. $4x + 15y = 7$
$\qquad\;\; 3x - 13y = 13$

_____  7. $7x + 2y = 11$
$\qquad\;\; 5x - 2y = 9$

_____  8. $3x + 3y = 5$
$\qquad\;\; -9x + 2y = 7$

_____  9. $54x + 33y = 27$
$\qquad\;\; 91x - 6y = 11$

_____  10. $6x - 2y = 7$
$\qquad\;\;\; 6x + 4y = 3$

**For each system choose the easiest variable to eliminate by adding and then write the multiplier for each equation to accomplish the elimination.**

_____  11. $3x - 4y = 6$
$\qquad\;\;\; 2x + y = 7$

_____  12. $5x - 3y = 8$
$\qquad\;\;\; 7x + 4y = 9$

_____  13. $53x + 24y = 11$
$\qquad\;\;\; 31x - 40y = 6$

_____  14. $6x + 4y = 7$
$\qquad\;\;\; x + 5y = 2$

_____  15. $-2x + 11y = 3$
$\qquad\;\;\; 5x + 9y = 7$

_____  16. $3x + 2y = 4$
$\qquad\;\;\; 5x + 8y = 11$

_____  17. $9x + 13y = 21$
$\qquad\;\;\; 6x - 17y = 22$

_____  18. $20x + 32y = 57$
$\qquad\;\;\; 22x - 4y = 30$

**Solve using the addition method.**

_____  19. $x + y = 5$
$\qquad\;\;\; 8x + y = 12$

_____  20. $4x - 3y = -4$
$\qquad\;\;\; x + 2y = 21$

_____  21. $3x - 2y = 0$
$\qquad\;\;\; 12x - 7y = 3$

_____ **22.** $2x + 5y = 2$
$\phantom{}$ $3x + 4y = 10$

_____ **23.** $12x + 9y = 9$
$\phantom{}$ $8x + 3y = -9$

_____ **24.** $5x - 4y = 6$
$\phantom{}$ $7x + 4y = 18$

_____ **25.** $5x + 2y = 13$
$\phantom{}$ $7x - 3y = -5$

# ■ Cumulative Review ·······························································································

**Simplify.**

_____ 1. $|-17|$

_____ 2. $\sqrt{49}$

_____ 3. $2 - 7$

_____ 4. $-8 \div (-4)$

_____ 5. $8 + 4 \cdot 9$

_____ 6. $2^{-3}$

_____ 7. $-\dfrac{13}{50} \cdot \dfrac{125}{52}$

_____ 8. $\dfrac{1}{27} + \dfrac{1}{30}$

_____ 9. $5x - 3x^2 + 2x - 7 + 4x^2 - 8$

_____ 10. $6(x - 2) + 2(x + 3)$

**Evaluate.**

_____ 11. $3x - y$ if $x = 3$ and $y = -2$

_____ 12. Find $F$ using $F = mv^2$ if $m = 10$ and $v = 3$.

**Check each value to see if it is a solution.**

_____ 13. $-3, 2x - 3 = 5 - 14$

_____ 14. $\dfrac{1}{2}, 6x + 5 \le 14x + 3$

_____ 15. $-5, |x| < 2$

_____ 16. $(2, 3), y = 4x - 5$

_____ 17. $(-1, 4), 3x + 2y > 5$

_____ 18. $2, x > 8$ or $x < 3$

_____ 19. $(5, 2), x + y = 7$
$\phantom{xxxxxxxxx} x - y = 3$

_____ 20. $(-1, 6), 5x - y < 2$
$\phantom{xxxxxxxxx} 3x - 2y > 15$

**Solve.**

_____ **21.** $5(x - 7) = 2x + 9$

_____ **22.** $3 - \frac{3}{40}x \geq \frac{7}{8}$

_____ **23.** $2x - 1 \geq 13$ and $5x - 1 > 14$

_____ **24.** $|2x - 1| = 5$

_____ **25.** $6x + 4(2 - x) = 5 - 3(7 - x)$

**Solve each system.**

_____ **26.** $3x + y = 4$
$x - 2y = 13$

_____ **27.** $8x + 14y = 6$
$12x + 21y = 5$

_____ **28.** $x + y \geq -2$
$-3x - y > -2$

**Graph on number lines or Cartesian planes as necessary.**

**29.** $3x - 5 = 7$

**30.** $2x + 3y = 12$

**32.** $5x - 3 \geq 2$

**33.** $|x| > 4$

**34.** $x + y > 1$
$x < 2$

**31.** $x - y = 1$
$y = \frac{2}{3}x$

**35.** $3x - y \geq 5$

***WORD PROBLEMS***

_____  **36.** Ben is nine years older than Karen. Twice Karen's age increased by Ben's age is 21. Find their ages.

_____  **37.** Marcy makes a floral bouquet of daisies and sea lavenders. Daisies sell for $1.50 each and sea lavenders for $1.80 each. If there are 10 flowers in the bouquet and it sells for $15.90, how many of each flower are used?

_____  **38.** A plane flies between two cities at 130 mph; a car goes the same distance at 30 mph. If the car took 8 hours longer, how far apart are the cities?

_____  **39.** Lisa makes two investments, one at 5% and one at 6% interest. She invests $100 more at 5%, but makes the same annual interest from each account. How much is in each?

**40.** Write from memory Numbers 23:19. _____

_____

_____

# CHAPTER 8
## Polynomials

## Bible: Multiplication

You have seen that multiplication occurs in the Bible literally, as in Leviticus 25:8. Another occurrence of literal multiplication, though perhaps not as obvious, occurs in Matthew 17:24-27.

1. How much did every person have to pay as a tribute or custom (check a

   study Bible)? _____

2. How much money did Peter give them for himself and Jesus?

   _____

3. What multiplication problem symbolizes this (include units)?

   _____

Read Luke 19:8. Let $x$ be the amount Zacchaeus stole by false accusation.

4. How much did he give back as restitution? _____

These literal examples of multiplication represent repeated additions. This leads to the idea of rapid growth. Multiplication has this more general sense in many passages in the Bible.

5. What does the command *to multiply* mean in passages such as Genesis

   1:22; 8:17; 9:1-7; 35:11? _____

6. God promised to multiply the seed of what people in these passages: Genesis 22:17; 26:4, 24; Joshua 24:3; Jeremiah 33:22?

   _____

7. What did God multiply in Acts 6:1, 7? _____

8. What is meant by *multiplication* in these verses: Deuteronomy 11:21;

   Proverbs 9:11; Job 29:18? _____

9. What is meant by *multiplication* in these verses: Job 34:37; 35:16;

   Ezekiel 35:13? _____

10. God also multiplies possessions. List verses in which possessions of
    different kinds were multiplied. _____

    _____

11. What is meant by *multiplication* in Job 35:6; Proverbs 29:16; Ezekiel
    16:51; and Amos 4:4? _____

    _____

12. Review Genesis 1:28 as a memory verse. Which of the above uses of
    multiplication is involved?

    _____

## Math History: Galileo

Galileo Galilei and Johannes Kepler were astronomers. Like Copernicus and Aristarchus, they used a lot of math.

1. When did Galileo live? _____

2. When did Kepler live? _____

3. Where was Galileo from? _____

4. Where was Kepler from? _____

Galileo was a math teacher, and in 1606 he published a pamphlet on mathematical computations. It was entitled "The Operation of the Geometric and Military Compasses."

5. Name two universities at which Galileo taught.

_____

6. What important object did Galileo invent for astronomy? _____

Later, Galileo published two important scientific books.

7. Name them.

_____

_____

8. Why was Galileo brought to trial?

_____

9. Name one of Galileo's "new sciences."

_____

Galileo had to study infinitely small things to develop his science.

10. What is the study of the infinitely small or large now called?

_____

11. Galileo recognized that the perfect squares could be matched with the natural numbers. Show a one-to-one correspondence to verify this.

_____

12. Kepler's most important book was _____

13. When was this published? _____

**14.** What were two important laws of astronomy that he discovered?

_____

_____

**15.** The area of an ellipse is found using the formula $A = \pi ab$. What kind of polynomial is contained in the formula? What degree does it have?

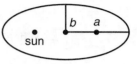

_____

**16.** Do you remember who took these important steps in astronomy?

    **A.** First to suggest that Earth orbits the sun  _____

    **B.** First modern to suggest that Earth orbits the sun  _____

    **C.** First to popularize that Earth orbits the sun  _____

    **D.** First to recognize that the orbits around the sun are ellipses  _____

## *Calculator Skills*

### POWERS

You are already familiar with the $\boxed{x^2}$ key on your calculator. $5.3006\boxed{x^2}$ yields 28.09636. This enables you to calculate $(5.3006)^2$ quickly and easily.

How can you compute $(5.3006)^3$? Some calculators have an $\boxed{x^3}$ key. If yours does, try it. It should work like the $\boxed{x^2}$ key. Did you get 148.92757? Most calculators don't have this key, but even if yours does it will not help you calculate $(5.3006)^7$. How can you calculate other powers of numbers? Look for the $\boxed{y^x}$ key and enter this sequence:

$5.3006$ $\boxed{y^x}$ $7$ $\boxed{=}$

Did you get 117,564.24?

Remember that multiplying and exponents come before additions when simplifying a numerical expression. Most calculators do this correctly. For the following problems do them by hand and then check that your calculator applies the correct order of operations.

$5 + 3 \cdot 7$ _____      $3 + 2 \cdot 7^2$ _____      $11 + 5 \cdot 3^3$ _____

$16 + 4^2$ _____      $6 - 2^5$ _____      $4^3 - 2 \cdot 3^4$ _____

Which is faster—the $\boxed{x^2}$ or $\boxed{y^x}$ method when calculating $(7.9)^2$? Using $\boxed{x^2}$ saves a keystroke. Now do $(4.7)^4$ with the $\boxed{y^x}$ key. Can you find $(4.7)^4$ using only the $\boxed{x^2}$ key? Applying the power property of exponents $(4.7)^4 = (4.7^2)^2$, you must square 4.7 twice $\boxed{x^2}\boxed{x^2}$. You could do eighth and sixteenth powers this way too. You could even do $(4.7)^{20}$ by using the memory to save $(4.7)^4$ and multiplying it by $(4.7)^{16}$ since by the multiplication property $(4.7)^4 \cdot (4.7)^{16} = (4.7)^{20}$. While squares and maybe fourth powers are faster with $\boxed{x^2}$, the $\boxed{y^x}$ key is certainly faster in general. Evaluate the polynomials below, making the best use of your calculator. Carry to 3 decimal places.

_____ **1.** $3x^2$ if $x = 4.7$

_____ **2.** $7x^3 + 5x^2$ if $x = 2.9$

_____ **3.** $5x^5 - 7x^4 + 3x^2 + 8$ if $x = 5.71$

_____ **4.** $x^{10} - 4x^9 + x^4 + 7x$ if $x = 3.1$

_____ **5.** $x^4 + x^2 + 7$ if $x = 7.7$

_____ **6.** $p^3q - 5pq + q^2$ if $p = 2.5$, $q = 1.5$

_____ **7.** $4y - 3z + y^2z - yz^2 + 6yz$ if $y = 2.1$, $z = 5.6$

_____ **8.** $3.2m^4 - \frac{4}{7}m^3 + m^2 - m + 5.1$ if $m = -1.6$

_____  **9.** $3.14r^3 - 2.718r^2 + 6.28r + 2.236$ if $r = 3.9$

_____  **10.** $stu - st - tu - su + s + t + u$ if $s = 8.3$, $t = 5.1$,
$u = 0.3$

# Polynomials in Brief

## *TERMINOLOGY*

The study of words and their origins is fascinating. Often you can determine the definition of a word if you know what the parts of the word mean. Most words in the English language come from words in other languages.

Consider these terms: *polynomial, monomial, binomial,* and *trinomial.* Each of these terms consists of two parts: a root and a prefix. Notice that the root word for each of these terms is *nomial,* which comes from the Greek word *nomos,* meaning "part." The prefixes indicate numerical values. Can you guess the value of each one?

The prefix *poly-* comes from Greek and means "much" or "many." Read the definition of *polynomial* found in the text.

1. Correlate the definition to the meaning of the original parts of the word. _____

2. How many other words with the prefix *poly-* can you think of?

   _____

3. The prefix *mono-* is also from Greek. What does it mean?_____

4. How many terms does a monomial have? _____

5. Define the following words by looking at the parts of the words.

   **a)** monotone       **c)** monochrome
   **b)** monoacid       **d)** monorail

   _____

6. Name some other words beginning with *mono-*.

   _____

7. You have seen the Latin prefixes *bi-*, meaning "two," and *tri-*, meaning "three," on many words you know: *bicycle* and *tricycle*; *bicentennial* and *tricentennial*; *bimonthly* and *trimonthly.* Tell what each of these words means.

   _____

When you come across new words that you do not know, look for any parts that you may know the meaning of. You will be surprised at how many new words you can learn by studying their etymologies. Be careful, though. Don't confuse similar roots and don't assume they will always occur as prefixes. Notice that *nomos* can also mean law or principle, because principles are parts of the order that God created.

**8.** Which prefixes, if any, occur in the following words?

| | | | |
|---|---|---|---|
| Carbon monoxide | _____ | trial | _____ |
| biology | _____ | monogram | _____ |
| astronomy | _____ | Bible | _____ |
| bifurcate | _____ | triceratops | _____ |
| triune | _____ | binary | _____ |
| monoceros | _____ | polysyllabic | _____ |
| metropolitan | _____ | triangle | _____ |
| bimodal | _____ | monolith | _____ |
| polyglot | _____ | ambidextrous | _____ |

# Polynomials Applied

## VELOCITY

1. Bill's science class measured the speed of falling objects. Complete the table.

| distance fallen in feet | after | number of seconds |
|---|---|---|
| 16 | | 1 |
| 64 | | 2 |
| 144 | | 3 |
| 256 | | 4 |
| ___ | | 5 |

2. Look for the pattern in these measurements. What is the GCF of the distances on the table? Divide each distance by the GCF and explain how the quotient is related to the corresponding number of seconds.

_____

_____ 3. How far will the object fall in *x* seconds?

_____ 4. How far would it fall in $\frac{1}{2}$ second?

_____ 5. The polynomial in question three describes the distance that an object falls after *x* seconds. What kind of polynomial is it?

If an object is dropped from a height of 300 feet,

_____ 6. how high will it be after 1 second?

_____ 7. how high will it be after 2 seconds?

_____ 8. how high will it be after *x* seconds?

If an object is dropped from a height of *h* feet,

_____ 9. how high will it be after *x* seconds?

_____ 10. What kind of polynomial is this?

Do you remember from your study of science what force caused the object to drop to the earth? God created gravity to allow objects to remain on or near the earth's surface. This force, therefore, will affect objects traveling in a vertical direction. Consider this force as you approach the questions that follow.

If a ball is thrown straight up (from sea level) without any gravity at a velocity of 130 feet per second, how high will it be

_____ 11. after 1 second?

_____ 12. after 2 seconds?

_____ **13.** after 4 seconds?

_____ **14.** after 8 seconds?

_____ **15.** after $x$ seconds?

If you throw the ball straight up at 130 feet per second, the ball would still try to go as far as the distances calculated in questions 11-15. Gravity, however, would tend to pull it down. Try to add the effect of gravity to redo the last five questions. How high would the ball be

_____ **16.** after 1 second?

_____ **17.** after 2 seconds?

_____ **18.** after 4 seconds?

_____ **19.** after 8 seconds?

_____ **20.** after $x$ seconds?

Suppose a ball is tossed vertically upward with a velocity of 120 ft./sec. but is thrown by someone standing on a building 100 ft. high. How high will the ball be

_____ **21.** after 5 seconds?

_____ **22.** after $x$ seconds?

_____ **23.** Suppose a bullet is shot upward at $v$ ft./sec. from a height of $h$ feet. How high is it after $x$ seconds?

_____ **24.** What type of polynomial is found in question 23? Also give the degree.

**25.** On January 28, 1986, the space shuttle *Challenger* exploded only 73 seconds after its liftoff from Cape Canaveral, Florida (at sea level). If its average speed was 630 feet per second, how high was it when it broke apart? Give your answer to the nearest thousand feet. Write an equation which would allow you to calculate the time, $t$, it would take the shuttle

to fall back to earth. _____

# Polynomials in Detail

## OPERATIONS AND PROPERTIES

Review the properties of real numbers. All of these properties apply to polynomials too. Instead of number examples, use $(x^2 + 5)$, $(x^3 - 3x)$, and $(x^2 - x - 1)$ to illustrate each property in the chart below.

| | property | of addition | of multiplication |
|---|---|---|---|
| **1.** | commutative | $(x^2 + 5) + (x^2 - x - 1)$ $= (x^2 - x - 1) + (x^2 + 5)$ | |
| **2.** | associative | | |
| **3.** | identity | | |
| **4.** | inverse | | |
| **5.** | zero | | |
| **6.** | distributive | | |

**7.** What polynomial is the identity for addition of polynomials? _____

**8.** What polynomial is the identity for multiplication of polynomials? _____

**9.** What polynomial is the additive inverse of $5x^4 - x^3 - 6x^2 + 8x - 1$?

_____

**10.** Show by vertical addition that they add up to the identity:

_____

**11.** What expression is the multiplicative inverse of $x^2 + 5$? _____

Now check your chart by simplifying both sides of each expression.

Example:

commutative property of addition: $\left.\begin{array}{l}(x^2 + 5) + (x^2 - x - 1) = 2x^2 - x + 4 \\ (x^2 - x - 1) + (x^2 + 5) = 2x^2 - x + 4\end{array}\right\}$ same.

**12.** commutative property of multiplication:

_____

**13.** associative property of addition: _____

**14.** associative property of multiplication:

_____

**15.** distributive property of multiplication:

_____

**16.** Finally, do some powers of a polynomial.

$(x + 1)^0$
$(x + 1)^1$
$(x + 1)^2$
$(x + 1)^3$
$(x + 1)^4$
$(x + 1)^5$

**17.** What would $(x + 1)^{-1}$ be? What would $(x + 1)^{-2}$ be? What is $(x + 1)^{10}$?

_____

_____

# ■ Practice

**POLYNOMIALS**

**Give the classification and degree of each polynomial.**

_____  **1.** $11x^2 - 5x + 7$    _____  **6.** $-97q^3r^2z^5$

_____  **2.** $x$    _____  **7.** $5x + 4y + 3z$

_____  **3.** $abc - def$    _____  **8.** $x^3 - 8x^4 + x - x^7$

_____  **4.** $p^3 + 1$    _____  **9.** $5xy - x^3y^5 + 9xy^2$

_____  **5.** $y^5 - y^4 + y^3 - y^2$    _____  **10.** $19 - 7p$

**Evaluate each polynomial if $x = -1, y = -3, z = 2$.**

_____  **11.** $x - y + z$    _____  **16.** $z^3 + 3z^2 - 5z + 1$

_____  **12.** $xy + yz - xz$    _____  **17.** $4x^9 - z^2$

_____  **13.** $4x^3 + 3y^2 - 2z$    _____  **18.** $x^7 + x^5 - x^4 + x^3 + x$

_____  **14.** $y^4 - 8y^2 + 2$    _____  **19.** $x^3y + yz^2$

_____  **15.** $3y^0$    _____  **20.** $\frac{5}{2}xyz$

**Add or subtract.**

_____  **21.** $(11x + 7y) + 6x$

_____  **22.** $(5xy - 3y) - (6xy - 2x)$

_____  **23.** $15ab^2 - 7ab^2$

_____  **24.** $(x + y) - (x - y)$

_____  **25.** $(4x^3 + 3x) + (x^3 - x^2 + x)$

_____  **26.** $(y^2 - 3y + 8) + (5y - y^2 + 1)$

_____  **27.** $(p^5 - 4p^3 + 3) - (p^4 + 3p^3 + p^2 - p + 2)$

_____  **28.** $(2x^3y - yz) + (x^3y + yz - x)$

_____  **29.** $7qrs - (5q^2 + qr + 9qrs - rs)$

_____  **30.** $(4y^2z - 3yz) + (5yz - 3y^2z)$

**Multiply.**

_____ **31.** $9x \cdot 4x$     _____ **36.** $\frac{1}{6}y^4z(-4y)$

_____ **32.** $2x^3 \cdot 3x \cdot 5x^2$     _____ **37.** $(3p^2)(2q)(7pq)$

_____ **33.** $\left(-\frac{15}{4}y^5\right)\left(\frac{32}{5}y^3\right)$     _____ **38.** $(5m^7)^3$

_____ **34.** $(x^2yz^2)\left(\frac{1}{2}xy^2z^3\right)$     _____ **39.** $(-xy^2)(-8x^3y)(-6x^2y^8)$

_____ **35.** $(-3p^2q^5)(-6p^7q)$     _____ **40.** $\left(\frac{2}{3}ab^3c^2\right)^4$

# ■ Practice

### MULTIPLYING POLYNOMIALS

**Multiply by distributing.**

_____ **1.** $7(y - 8)$

_____ **2.** $6z(5z + 7)$

_____ **3.** $11xy(3x^2 - 5xy)$

_____ **4.** $7x^2(4y^2 + 3z + 1)$

_____ **5.** $-2x(x^2 - x + 1)$

_____ **6.** $3n^3(5n^2 - 8)$

_____ **7.** $8xy(x^2 + xy - 3y^2)$

_____ **8.** $-4v(5v^3 - 4v^2 + 3v + 7)$

_____ **9.** $\frac{1}{3}(6p - 15p^8 + 3 + 9p^5)$

_____ **10.** $\frac{1}{2}xyz(8x + y + 2z)$

**Multiply these binomial products.**

_____ **11.** $(x + 8)(x - 1)$     _____ **16.** $(5s - t)(5s + t)$

_____ **12.** $(y - 5)(3y - 2)$     _____ **17.** $(7v + 12)(v - 6)$

_____ **13.** $(4x + 7)(2x + 11)$     _____ **18.** $(3x^2 + 4)(7x - 5)$

_____ **14.** $(5p - 3)(11p + 14)$     _____ **19.** $(b + 8)(b + 8)$

_____ **15.** $(pq + 1)(p - q)$     _____ **20.** $(x - 15)(x + 2)$

**Multiply these special polynomial products.**

**21.** $5x^2 \cdot 13x^3$ _____

**22.** $7x^2y \cdot 11xy^3z$ _____

**23.** $(8x - 3)(x^2 - 5x + 2)$ _____

**24.** $(x^2 + y)(y^3 - x^2y + 3)$ _____

**25.** $(p - 17)^2$ _____

**26.** $(4z - 2)^2$ _____

**27.** $(3x + 5y)(3x - 5y)$ _____

**28.** $(12 - y)(12 + y)$ _____

**29.** $(q + 6)(5q - 30)$ _____

**30.** $(x^2 - 1)(x^4 + x^2 + 1)$ _____

**Multiply.**

_____ **31.** $-7x^3 \cdot 5x^2$

_____ **32.** $-8x^2y(3xy - 5x^2y + xy^3)$

_____ **33.** $(2x - 3)(7x + 4)$

_____ **34.** $(7c + 3)^2$

_____ **35.** $(3p - 5)(3p + 5)$

_____ **36.** $(-9q^3rs^4)(-6q^2rs^5 + r)$

_____ **37.** $(11x - 3y)(4x + 7y)$

_____ **38.** $(m + 2)(3m^2 - 5m + 6)$

_____ **39.** $(4d - 11f)^2$

_____ **40.** $(3xy^2z^3)^4$

# ■ Practice

### DIVIDING POLYNOMIALS

**Divide the monomials.**

_____ **1.** $56a^2bc \div 14ac$   _____ **6.** $\dfrac{16abc}{16abc}$

_____ **2.** $\dfrac{4}{3}r^5 \div 2r^3$   _____ **7.** $44s^7t^5u^3 \div 4s^3t^4u$

_____ **3.** $20xy^2z \div \dfrac{1}{2}x$   _____ **8.** $\dfrac{-62m^5n^4}{2m^3n}$

_____ **4.** $\dfrac{-8p^3q}{-2q}$   _____ **9.** $-48xy \div (-3x)$

_____ **5.** $\dfrac{x^8}{x^2}$   _____ **10.** $\dfrac{24h^5k^2}{-3h^4k}$

**Divide by the monomial.**

_____ **11.** $(18x^2 + 12xy) \div 6x$

_____ **12.** $(m^5 - m^4 + m^3) \div m^2$

_____ **13.** $(49y^4 - 14) \div 7$

_____ **14.** $(13a^2 + 26a^3 + 13a) \div 13a$

_____ **15.** $\dfrac{9p^2q^2r - 12pq^3r + 18pq^2r^3}{3pq^2r}$

_____ **16.** $(6n^9 - 2n^7 - 8n^6) \div 2n^4$

_____ **17.** $(z^4 - 6z^2) \div z^2$

_____ **18.** $(9kh - 6k^2) \div (-3k)$

_____ **19.** $(132x^2 - 36x + 60) \div 12$

_____ **20.** $\dfrac{rst^2 - r^2st + r^2t^2 - rs^2t}{rt}$

**Divide the polynomials.**

_____ **21.** $(x^2 - 5x + 8) \div (x + 1)$

_____ **22.** $(2x^3 + x + 7) \div (x - 5)$

_____ **23.** $(x^3 - 8) \div (x^2 + 4)$

_____ **24.** $(y^2 + 10y + 24) \div (y + 6)$

_____ **25.** $(12a^2 + 8ab - 7b^2) \div (2a + 3b)$

_____ **26.** $(6y^3 + 17y^2 - 3y - 20) \div (2y + 5)$

_____ **27.** $(18y^2 + 27y - 56) \div (3y + 8)$

_____  **28.** $(x^4 - x^3 + 4x^2 + 3) \div (x^2 + 2x - 5)$

_____  **29.** $(3x^5 + 7x^3 + 9) \div (x^2 + 4)$

_____  **30.** $(z - 10) \div (z + 2)$

# ■ Cumulative Review

**Match each integer to the type. Use each answer once.**

_____ **1.** $\sqrt{9} - \sqrt{9}$        **A.** Complex (not real)

_____ **2.** $\dfrac{9}{\sqrt{9}}$        **B.** Integer

_____ **3.** $\sqrt{99}$        **C.** Natural

_____ **4.** $\sqrt{-9}$        **D.** Rational

_____ **5.** $\dfrac{\sqrt{9}}{9}$        **E.** Real

_____ **6.** $-\sqrt{9}$        **F.** Whole

_____ **7.** Write *xxxxx* using exponents.

_____ **8.** Simplify $x^{-3}$.

_____ **9.** How many solutions does a dependent system have?

_____ **10.** Find the slope of the line through $(2, 6)$ and $(4, 5)$.

_____ **11.** Solve $5x + 2 = 51$.

_____ **12.** Seven times a number is at least six less than ten times a number. Find the number.

_____ **13.** Simplify $(x^2 + 3x - 4) + (x^2 - 7x + 6)$.

_____ **14.** Evaluate $Q = pr^2 + sp - 5$ for $Q$ if $p = -2$, $r = 3, s = \dfrac{1}{2}$.

_____ **15.** Give the degree of $5x - 3x^2 + 7$.

_____ **16.** Simplify $(x - 3)(x + 7)$.

_____ **17.** Solve $4x < 8$ and $-3x \geq 6$.

_____ **18.** If $y$ varies directly with $x$ and $y$ is 20 when $x$ is $\dfrac{1}{3}$, find $y$ when $x$ is $\dfrac{5}{12}$.

_____ **19.** Solve for $x$: $3rx - st = u - v$.

**20.** The school play sold 210 tickets. Adult tickets sold for \$2 and children's tickets for \$1. How many of each were sold if they collected \$286 in ticket sales?

**21.** Simplify $(3x + 2)(x^2 + 2x - 1)$. _____

**22.** Graph $y = -\frac{3}{4}x + 8$.

**23.** Divide $(x^2 + 3x - 4) \div (x + 1)$. _____

**24.** Solve the system $\begin{aligned} 3x + 2y &= -9 \\ 5x - 7y &= -46 \end{aligned}$ _____

**25.** Simplify $\dfrac{8x^2 - 6x + 10x^3}{2x}$. _____

**26.** Solve $|x - 5| > 7$. _____

**27.** Find the equation of the line through $(5, -5)$ with slope $-\frac{3}{5}$.

_____

**28.** Graph $x < 3$ on a number line.

**29.** The perimeter of a rectangle is 46″. The length is two more than five times the width. Find the dimensions. _____

**30.** Graph the system $\begin{aligned} x - y &< 3 \\ 2x - 7y &\le -14 \end{aligned}$

**31.** Simplify $(5x^2 - 3x - 7) - (2x^2 - 8x + 1)$. _____

**32.** What is the slope of a horizontal line? _____

**33.** Solve $\frac{2}{51}x + \frac{5}{9} = \frac{7}{153}$. _____

**34.** Find $|3(-7) - 4|$. _____

**35.** Simplify $2 \cdot 6 - 2 \cdot 4 + 7 \cdot 3^2$. _____

**36.** Evaluate $\dfrac{3x - 4}{5}$ if $x = -7$. _____

**37.** Classify the polynomial $5x^3y^2$. _____

**38.** In which quadrant is $(4, -2)$? _____

**39.** A boat goes 10 miles upstream in 3 hours and 12 miles downstream in 2 hours. Find the speed of the boat and the speed of the current.

_____

**40.** Write from memory II Corinthians 5:21.

_____

_____

_____

# CHAPTER 9
## Factoring Polynomials

## Bible: Division

Did you know that division occurs in the Bible? I Kings 7:3-5 and Judges 7:16-19 provide examples of literal division. The passage in Judges 7 divides 300 men into three groups of 100 each. Notice that the 3 groups of men are separated from each other and the men are grouped into equal portions. Mathematical division includes these concepts: separation, allotment, and equal portions.

Look up the following verses and decide which of the division concepts are intended in each context. What is being divided in each?

1. Genesis 1:4-18 _____
2. Exodus 14:16, 21 _____
3. Leviticus 11:4-7, 26 _____
4. Numbers 26:53-56 _____
5. Deuteronomy 14:7 _____
6. Joshua 18:5, 10 _____
7. I Kings 3:25-26 _____
8. I Chronicles 26:1, 12, 19 _____
9. Psalm 74:13; 78:13 _____
10. Ezekiel 5:1-2 _____
11. Matthew 12:25-26; Mark 3:24-26; Luke 11:17-18 _____
12. Luke 12:13-14 _____
13. Luke 12:51-53 _____
14. John 7:43; 9:16; 10:19 _____
15. Acts 14:4 _____
16. Romans 16:17 _____
17. I Corinthians 1:10 _____
18. I Corinthians 3:3; 11:18 _____

**19.** Hebrews 4:12 _____

**20.** Revelation 16:19 _____

Look closely at each of the verses below. What is meant by division in each?

**21.** I Corinthians 12:11 _____

**22.** II Timothy 2:15 _____

**23.** Review Judges 7:16 as a memory verse. What ideas of division are

central to this verse? _____

# Math History: Fibonacci

Fibonacci studied a certain class of sequences. He discovered many properties of sequences in which each term is obtained by adding the previous two. Do you see that if you are given two numbers such as 2 and 6, you could construct a sequence by adding? Add $2 + 6 = 8$ to get the third term. Now, the fourth term is $6 + 8 = 14$. Continuing, you get this sequence:

2, 6, 8, 14, 22, 36, 58, 94, . . .

Construct a sequence of this kind that begins with

  **1.** 3, 4 _____

  **2.** 5, 1 _____

The most famous of these sequences is called the Fibonacci sequence. Its first 2 terms are 1 and 1.

  **3.** Give the Fibonacci sequence. _____

  **4.** What was Fibonacci's real name? _____

  **5.** Where was he from? _____

  **6.** When did he live? _____

  **7.** What was his most famous book? _____

  **8.** When was it published? _____

  **9.** What kinds of problems did Fibonacci discuss in his book?

_____

Fibonacci liked to use fractions with a numerator of 1. These are called unit fractions.

  **10.** What fraction would he have expressed by this sum: $\frac{1}{2} + \frac{1}{4} + \frac{1}{5} + \frac{1}{50}$

_____

Fibonacci's famous sequence arose from a problem of growth in rabbit populations. It begins with one pair of baby rabbits. After 2 months (in the third month) the rabbits have matured to adults and have a pair of baby rabbits. The next (fourth) month the adults have two more babies, and the previous babies are "teens." (There are 3 pairs total now.) By the fifth month, the "teens" are now adults and have babies while the original adults also have babies. Thus, there are 2 new baby pairs, the previous baby pair is in its "teens," and there are 2 pairs of adults.

**11.** If rabbits are always born in pairs as babies, grow to teens in a month, and mature and produce a pair of babies each month thereafter, complete the chart below for rabbit populations up to the 9th month. Where does the Fibonacci sequence occur?

| | Month 1 | 2 | 3 | 4 | 5 | 6 | 7 | 8 | 9 |
|---|---|---|---|---|---|---|---|---|---|
| Babies | | | | | | | | | |
| Teens | | | | | | | | | |
| Adults | | | | | | | | | |
| Total | | | | | | | | | |

# *Calculator Skills*

## STATISTICS

Your calculator can perform some of the statistical calculations that you have learned. Look for these keys (remember that notation above a key requires you to press the 2nd or Shift key).

DATA = key for entering a score
$n$ = the number of scores entered so far
$\Sigma x$ = the sum of the scores
$\bar{x}$ = the mean of the scores (some calculators use $\mu$)
$\sigma$ = the standard deviation of the scores

Other statistical keys such as $\Sigma xy$, $\Sigma x^2$, $s$, $r$, and $\hat{m}$ are used in more advanced statistical applications.

Now that you have found the keys, do you see how to use them? On some calculators they will require 2nd, while on other calculators a special statistics mode is needed. To enter statistics mode, look for a STAT key. This key may be the same as pressing 2nd C, or it may require MODE 3. If you need to press mode and a number, the list of modes at the top of the calculator will tell you the correct number. To get out of statistics mode, you may need to press CA, STAT, or MODE 0. If you cannot figure out entering or exiting statistics mode, check the instructions for your calculator.

Your teacher mentions that the test scores on last week's test were 73, 88, 95, 77, and 84. You can analyze this data by entering statistics mode. Type 73, then press DATA (usually the same as the M+ button). Do not worry if a 1 comes onto your display—the calculator is just counting the scores. Continue entering the other four test scores: 88 DATA 95 DATA 77 DATA 84 DATA.

Press $\boxed{\Sigma x}$ to find the total of these five test scores (417). Press $\boxed{n}$ to find the number of scores (5). Press $\boxed{\bar{x}}$ (or $\mu$) to find the mean (83.4), which is the same as finding $\boxed{\Sigma x} \boxed{\div} \boxed{n}$. Press $\boxed{\sigma_n}$ to find the standard deviation (7.81281).

Now press 63 DATA. Notice that there are now six values (press $\boxed{n}$ to verify). Entering data does not start over; the calculator includes 63 with the previous five test scores. You should find that $\boxed{\Sigma x}$ = 480, $\boxed{\bar{x}}$ = 80, and $\boxed{\sigma_n}$ = 10.424331. In order to start a new problem, you will have to clear the whole statistical memory. Try CA, exit statistics mode, or check the instruction book.

Find $\Sigma x$, $\bar{x}$, and $\sigma_n$ for each set of scores below (carry to 2 decimal places).

**1.** 46, 73, 18 _____

**2.** 97, 44, 100, 89 _____

**3.** 57, 66, 45, 80 _____

**4.** 94, 86, 88, 97, 91, 60 _____

**5.** 83, 93, 77, 88, 86, 85, 93, 84, 88, 87, 93, 90, 89, 83, 85, 91, 79, 96, 99, 92, 79, 84

_____

**6.** 509, 621, 538, 614 _____

**7.** 8, 7, 5, 8, 6, 9, 4, 3, 8, 9, 10, 7, 8, 8, 9, 6, 7, 8, 0, 5, 8, 9, 8, 7, 8

_____

**8.** 24, 16, 25, 18, 31, 30, 27 _____

# Factoring in Brief: Summary

Are you surprised at how much factoring you have done in algebra? Think about all the times you have factored whole numbers.

1. Factor completely into primes: 7938 _____

2. Find the GCF of 42 and 56. _____

3. Find the LCM of 42 and 56. _____

4. Reduce $\frac{56}{32}$. _____

5. Add $\frac{7}{110} + \frac{5}{66}$. _____

6. Multiply $\frac{17}{8} \cdot \frac{20}{51}$. _____

7. Solve $\frac{x}{6} - 1 = \frac{1}{15}$. _____

8. Can you explain how factoring was used in questions 2-3?

   _____

9. Which problems used LCMs in questions 4-7? How were they used?

   _____

10. How did the other problems use the GCF? _____

    _____

11. The variables of $27x^2y$ are already factored. How can you completely

    factor the monomial? _____

The GCF of $36x^2y$ and $40xy^3$ is $4xy$.
The LCM of $36x^2y$ and $40xy^3$ is $360x^2y^3$.

12. Use the GCF to reduce $\frac{36x^2y}{40xy^3}$ (cancel variables like numbers). _____

13. Multiply $\frac{15x}{4} \cdot \frac{12}{5x}$. _____

Adding $\frac{1}{4x^3} + \frac{1}{3x^3}$ will require obtaining fractions having the common denominator $12x^3$, and solving $\frac{2}{3x} + 3 = \frac{5}{2x}$ will require multiplying both sides by $6x$. The LCM is used in both instances.

14. Factor $18x^4 - 3x^3 - 45x^2$ completely. Did you use the GCF or LCM?

    _____

As you improve your skills, you will learn to apply factoring to other problems. The GCF and LCM are needed when working with rational expressions too. Which do you think will be used to do the following problems?

**15.** Reduce $\dfrac{9x^3 - 25x}{18x^4 - 3x^3 - 45x}$. _____

**16.** Add $\dfrac{x + 2}{9x^3 - 25x} + \dfrac{x - 1}{18x^4 - 3x^3 - 45x}$. _____

**17.** Multiply $\dfrac{x^3 + 1}{x^2 + 2x + 1} \cdot \dfrac{x^2 + 4x + 3}{x^2 - x + 1}$. _____

**18.** Solve $\dfrac{1}{x^2 - 1} - 2 = \dfrac{1}{x^2 + x + 1}$. _____

# Factoring Applied

## SALES TAX

1. What property permits you to factor out common factors?

_____

_____

Two checking accounts each pay 6% interest annually. One account has no minimum balance and no service charge on traveler's checks, but there is a fee for each check used. The other account has a fee for traveler's checks, requires a minimum balance of $300, but provides free checks. Don realizes that it could be beneficial to have money in both accounts—that way he could put most of his money in the second account to get free checking, but he could have some money in the first account to be able to get traveler's checks for his mission trip next summer without paying a fee. Although Don sees benefits for splitting his money, he is not sure if he will earn less interest that way.

2. Use algebra to answer Don's question if $x$ and $y$ are the amounts deposited in each account.

_____

_____

Sandy and Cheryl are shopping. They are thrifty and enjoy getting good deals. As the cashier begins to enter Sandy's items, Cheryl asks, "Maybe I should put my items with yours so that we could save tax by combining our merchandise. What do you think?" Since Sandy is in algebra class, she can figure out which way is better.

3. If the state and city sales taxes combine to 8% in their state, what answer should Sandy give to Cheryl?

_____

Factoring can help in many situations. How do you add 1600 + 5700 + 2400 + 1500 + 1300? You can use factoring to obtain the sum. Rewrite the problem by factoring out 100 and combining the factors by grouping the easiest pairs.

$$100(16 + 24 + 57 + 13 + 15) = 100(125) = 12{,}500$$

The method is the same for estimating 1601.3 + 5699.1 + 2403.5 + 1502.4 + 1298.7 when you notice that all the terms are close to a multiple of 100. The same idea can be done for multiples of seven:

$$35.41 + 76.91 + 42.23 + 56.9 = 7(5 + 11 + 6 + 8) = 7(30) = 210$$

**Use the common factors to find the sums in your head.**

_____  **4.** $340 + 560 + 230 + 480$

_____  **5.** $56 + 48 + 80 + 24$

_____  **6.** $720 + 800 + 930 + 470$

_____  **7.** $26 + 39 + 13 + 52$

_____  **8.** $22 + 121 + 77 + 132$

_____  **9.** $81 + 36 + 63$

**Use the common factor idea for estimating each sum.**

_____  **10.** $5.9 + 18.1 + 36.4 + 20.8$

_____  **11.** $410.1 + 431.3 + 220.2 + 349.6$

_____  **12.** $2603.7 + 1300.4 + 2598.3$

_____  **13.** $6800.3 + 3400.1 + 5090.8$

# Factoring in Detail

## CUBE FORMULAS

You have learned a lot about factoring, but how would you factor $x^3 - 8$ or $x^3 - x^2 + 2x + 2$? This worksheet will introduce you to more factoring methods.

Do you recall how you learned to factor the difference of squares? You multiplied $(a - b)(a + b)$ and discovered that the answer was $a^2 - b^2$, a difference of two perfect squares. Perform these two products and write the factoring formula for each. What would you name them?

**1.** $(a - b)(a^2 + ab + b^2)$ _____

**2.** $(a + b)(a^2 - ab + b^2)$ _____

**Use your formulas to factor these problems.**

**3.** $x^3 - 8$ _____

**4.** $y^3 + 27$ _____

**5.** $64x^3 + 1$ _____

**6.** $8y^{12} - 27x^9$ _____

Factor these *completely*. Be careful; each requires multiple steps. Check for squares before cubes.

**7.** $81x^{10} + 3x^7$ _____

**8.** $2x^6 - 128$ _____

Now look at $x^3 - x^2 + 2x - 2$. This polynomial has four terms. Look at the method of grouping used below:

$$x^3 - x^2 + 2x - 2$$
$$(x^3 - x^2) + (2x - 2) \quad \text{group}$$
$$x^2(x - 1) + 2(x - 1) \quad \text{factor common factors in each group}$$
$$(x - 1)(x^2 + 2) \quad \text{factor the common factor } (x - 1)$$

**Use this grouping method to factor each of these problems.**

_____ **9.** $x^5 + 3x^3 + 4x^2 + 12$

_____ **10.** $xy + 2y - 3x - 6$

**11.** Why can't the grouping method be used to factor $x^3 + 4x^2 + 3x + 15$?

_____

# ■ Practice

### COMMON FACTORS AND DIFFERENCES OF SQUARES

**Factor out the common factors.**

_____  **1.** $11x + 44$

_____  **2.** $15x^3 - 9x^2$

_____  **3.** $14z^2 - 42$

_____  **4.** $12z^3 + 36z^2 - 6z$

_____  **5.** $a^3b + a^2b^2 + a^2b^3$

_____  **6.** $34ab^2 - 17a^2b + 51a^3b^2 + 68ab$

_____  **7.** $121y^5 - 132y^3$

_____  **8.** $100r^9s^8t^5 - 60r^6s^7t^9$

_____  **9.** $24x^2 - 32xy + 40y^2$

_____  **10.** $18m^3 - 10m^2 + 63m$

**Factor each difference of squares. Remember to factor out common factors first.**

_____  **11.** $y^2 - 81$   _____  **16.** $p^{10} - q^{24}$

_____  **12.** $16s^2 - 49t^2$   _____  **17.** $r^2 - 256$

_____  **13.** $169a^6b^2 - 1$   _____  **18.** $h^4k^2 - m^2n^4$

_____  **14.** $25x^4 - 144y^6$   _____  **19.** $196x^2 - 100$

_____  **15.** $64z^8 - 9$   _____  **20.** $c^5 - c^3$

**Factor.**

**21.** $9x^4 - 1$ _____

**22.** $9x^4 - 6x^3$ _____

**23.** $9x^4 - 15x^3 + 24x^2 - 12x + 3$ _____

**24.** $9x^4 - 36x^2$ _____

**25.** $a^3b^5 - a^4b^4 + a^4b^5$ _____

**26.** $3m^2 - 27$ _____

**27.** $36t^2 - 121v^2$ _____

**28.** $100 - 64z^2$ _____

**29.** $98pq^3rs^2 - 28p^2q^3rs^3 + 70p^2q^2r^2s^2$ _____

**30.** $3y^5 + 75y$ _____

# Practice

### FACTORING TRINOMIALS

**Factor the perfect square trinomials.**

_____ **1.** $y^2 + 36y + 324$

_____ **2.** $z^2 - 10z + 25$

_____ **3.** $9x^2 - 66x + 121$

_____ **4.** $81r^2 + 72r + 16$

_____ **5.** $36s^2 - 84st + 49t^2$

_____ **6.** $h^4 + 26h^2 + 169$

**Factor.**

_____ **7.** $x^2 + 3x - 40$

_____ **8.** $c^2 - 5c - 66$

_____ **9.** $t^2 + 24t + 63$

_____ **10.** $y^2 - 18y + 56$

_____ **11.** $m^2 + 17m - 200$

_____ **12.** $x^2 - 18x + 65$

**Factor.**

_____ **13.** $14n^2 - 57n - 27$

_____ **14.** $15z^2 + 44z + 32$

_____ **15.** $2s^2 + 3s - 35$

_____ **16.** $4v^2 - 33v + 54$

_____ **17.** $36x^2 + 81x - 40$

_____ **18.** $15a^2 + 13a + 2$

**Factor the common factors first and then the trinomial.**

_____ **19.** $2x^2 + 16x + 32$

_____ **20.** $3y^3 - 3y^2 - 6y$

_____ **21.** $42p^3 + 49p^2 - 21p$

_____ **22.** $2b^5 + 7b^4 - 72b^3$

_____ **23.** $6x^3 + x^2 - 70x$

_____ **24.** $36d^2 - 24dk + 4k^2$

**Factor.**

_____ **25.** $x^7 - 9x^6 + 14x^5$

_____ **26.** $4x^2 - 60xy - 99y^2$

_____ **27.** $15q^3 + 50q^2 - 40q$

_____ **28.** $16k^2 + 56k + 49$

_____ **29.** $z^2 - 10z - 96$

_____ **30.** $3p^2 - 54p + 243$

# ■ Practice

### FACTORING COMPLETELY

I. Factor common factors.

II How many terms are there?

    A. Two — look for a difference of squares

    B. Three — is it a perfect square trinomial

               — otherwise use trial and error

    C. Four or more — factor by grouping

III. Repeat step two until further factoring is impossible.

### DECISION TREE

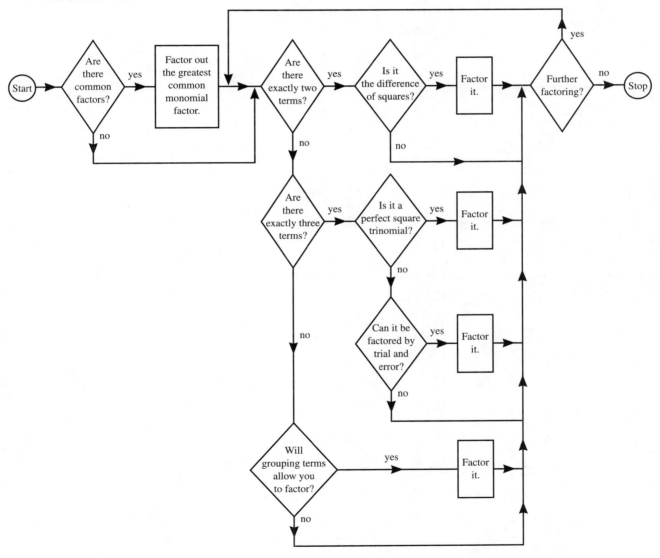

*Reminders*

1. Factoring is not simplifying—(2 · 3 is not simplest form, 6 is).

2. Factoring is important because it is a key step for other processes:

    (1) reduce fractions

(2) multiply and divide fractions

(3) add and subtract fractions

(4) solve fractional equations

(5) simplify radicals

3. Factor only when instructed to unless it is necessary to achieve a goal in step 2.

**FACTOR COMPLETELY.**

_____ **1.** $6s^2 + 51s + 24$

_____ **2.** $16z^2 + 8z + 1$

_____ **3.** $8y^2 - 72$

_____ **4.** $8n^2 - 26n + 15$

_____ **5.** $18f^4 - 27f^3 + 8f$

_____ **6.** $5m^2 + 19mn - 4n^2$

_____ **7.** $x^2y^2 - 9xy^2 + 14y^2$

_____ **8.** $9e^2 - 64$

_____ **9.** $6j^2 + 48j + 42$

_____ **10.** $9b^3c - 48b^2c^2 + 64bc^3$

_____ **11.** $24p^2 - 74pq + 45q^2$

_____ **12.** $49d^4 - 16d^3$

_____ **13.** $26x^4y + 2x^4y^2 - 14x^3y^3$

_____ **14.** $126t^5 + 231t^4 - 210t^3$

_____ **15.** $48k^4 - 300k^2$

_____ **16.** $c^2d^2 + 4cdf + 3f^2$

_____ **17.** $z^2 + 19z + 60$

_____ **18.** $a^3bc + 3a^2b^2c + 2ab^3c$

_____ **19.** $2w^2 + 8w - 504$

_____ **20.** $2g^3h^3i + 2g^2h^4i$

_____ **21.** $6x^4y + 8x^3y^2z - 8x^2y^3z^2$

_____ **22.** $18p^2 - 132p + 242$

_____ **23.** $u^2 - 2uv - 8v^2$

_____ **24.** $x^2 + x - 132$

_____ **25.** $81q^2r - r^3$

# ■ Cumulative Review ...............................................................

1. What quadrant is $(-3, 1)$ in? _____

2. What is the degree of the polynomial $5 + x^3 - 7x$? _____

3. Name the property: $\frac{7}{3} \cdot \frac{3}{7} = 1$. _____

4. What kind of number is 2.4? _____

5. $\{5, 7, 11\} \cup \{6, 7, 9, 11\}$ _____

**Graph. Use a number line or the Cartesian plane as needed.**

6. $-6$

7. $2x + 3y = 15$

8. $\left(-\frac{2}{3}, 2\right)$

9. $2x + 7 \leq 4 - x$

**10.** $3x - y < 5$
  $x + 2y > 6$

**Simplify.**

**11.** $(x^5 + 3x^3 - 5x^2 + 2) - (x^5 + 3x^4 + 5x^2 + 2)$ _____

**12.** $(2x - 7)(9x - 4)$ _____

**13.** $\dfrac{35x^3y^2 - 10x^2y^2 + 70x^2y^3}{5x^2y}$ _____

**14.** $27x^5y^{11}(3x - 4x^8y^3 + 6y^5)$ _____

**15.** $(3x - 1)^2$ _____

**Factor.**

_____ **16.** $x^2 + 3x - 40$

_____ **17.** $4x^2 - y^2$

_____ **18.** $5x^3 + 20x^2 + 20x$

_____ **19.** $2x^2 - 11x + 12$

_____ **20.** $3x + 6 + xy + 2y$

**Evaluate.**

_____  **21.** $5 + 2 \cdot 3 - 4(2 + 5)$

_____  **22.** $6 \cdot 2^{-3}$

_____  **23.** $\dfrac{13}{96} - \dfrac{11}{80}$

_____  **24.** $\sqrt{x + 1}$ if $x = 3$

_____  **25.** $V = 4xy + 2x^2$; find $V$ if $x = 3$ and $y = 5$.

**Solve.**

_____  **26.** $\dfrac{2}{5}x - \dfrac{1}{4} = \dfrac{1}{10}$

_____  **27.** $|4x + 1| \geq 5$

_____  **28.** $x = 2y + 3$
  $2x - 5y = 7$

_____  **29.** $3x + 11y = -16$
  $7x - 2y = 101$

_____  **30.** $A = nw$ for $w$

**Find the slope of the line**

_____  **31.** when $y = 3x - 5$.

_____  **32.** passing through $(-1, -5)$ and $(5, -3)$.

**Find the equation of the line that**

_____  **33.** is vertical through $(2, 3)$.

_____  **34.** has slope $-\dfrac{2}{5}$ and $y$-intercept $(0, 4)$.

_____  **35.** has slope $-2$ and passes through $(4, -1)$.

_____  **36.** is parallel to $y = \dfrac{1}{2}x + 4$ and contains $(2, -2)$.

**Word Problems.**

**37.** Three consecutive numbers add up to 54. Find the numbers.

**38.** Two cars left Shreveport at 50 mph going in opposite directions. One car traveled two hours longer to reach its destination. How long did each travel if their destinations were 500 miles apart?

_____

**39.** Mark invested $600 and earns annual interest of $42.60. How much did he invest at 5% and how much at 8%?

_____

**40.** Write from memory Genesis 1:28. _____

_____

_____

_____

_____

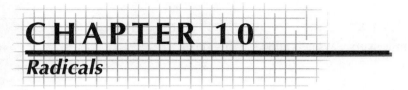

# CHAPTER 10
## Radicals

## Bible: Addition

Addition occurs in the Bible in a literal sense in Numbers 2:9, 16, 24, 31, and 32. This passage includes the addition of twelve terms with four subtotals and a grand total. Mathematical addition also appears in Genesis 5.

_____    **1.** Write the addition problem in Genesis 5:12-14.

_____    **2.** Write the addition problem in Genesis 5:28-31.

**These examples of addition emphasize the idea of increase. Many passages use the word _addition_ in this less technical sense. The use of addition denotes increase in each passage below. Identify the increasing quantity in each.**

**3.** Acts 2:47 _____

**4.** Psalm 69:27 _____

**5.** Matthew 6:27 _____

**6.** Jeremiah 45:3 _____

**7.** Isaiah 38:5 _____

**8.** Proverbs 16:23 _____

**9.** Deuteronomy 4:2 _____

**10.** II Peter 1:5 _____

**The passages below use various words to communicate the idea of addition or increase. Identify the word or phrase and then the increasing quantity.**

**11.** James 4:6 _____

**12.** Psalm 73:12 _____

**13.** Esther 4:7 _____

**14.** Philippians 1:16 _____

**15.** Luke 20:47 _____

**16.** Numbers 4:2 _____

**17.** Review Matthew 6:33 as a memory verse. What is added in this verse, and what does it mean?

_____

_____

# Math History: Pythagoras

In this chapter you learned a proof of the Pythagorean theorem. Pythagoras and his followers knew of this theorem as well as Pythagorean triples of integers that satisfy it.

1. When did Pythagoras live? _____

2. Where was he from? _____

3. Do any of Pythagoras' writings remain for us to read today? _____

4. Complete the one statement of Pythagoras that is probably authentic:

    "All is _____." _____

The quote above shows how religiously Pythagoras and his followers viewed math. The harmony in math played a role in their rituals.

5. While their religious devotion to numbers was wrong, why were they able to recognize harmony in the number system?

    _____

6. The Pythagoreans even recognized math in music. If you pluck a string that sounds the note C, how could you make the same note an octave

    higher? _____

7. The Pythagoreans apparently studied properties
   of a favorite geometrical shape (polygon).
   They often drew a star inside this shape.
   What shape was this? Draw it.              _____

The Pythagoreans also studied perfect, abundant, and deficient numbers by adding all the factors of a number.

6 is *perfect* since its factors 1, 2, and 3 add up to itself: $1 + 2 + 3 = 6$.
4 is *deficient* since its factors 1 and 2 come up short: $1 + 2 < 4$.
12 is *abundant* since its factors add up to more than itself:
$$1 + 2 + 3 + 4 + 6 > 12.$$

8. Find the next perfect number after 6 and classify all the numbers in between as deficient or abundant.

    _____

Thales preceded Pythagoras and may have made the first mathematical proofs, thus earning the title of "the first mathematician."

9. When did this mathematician live? _____

10. Where was he from? _____

## *Calculator Skills*

### RADICALS

Square roots are easy to find on a calculator. Just press the $\boxed{\sqrt{\phantom{x}}}$ key ($\boxed{\text{INV}}$ $\boxed{x^2}$ on some calculators). Round to 2 decimal places if necessary. Find the following.

_____    **1.** $\sqrt{64009}$        _____    **3.** $\sqrt{657}$

_____    **2.** $\sqrt{483}$        _____    **4.** $\sqrt{7569}$

Remember that $\sqrt[5]{17}$ means the same as $17^{\frac{1}{5}}$. This means that you can use your exponent key to find radicals. Since 1 $\boxed{\div}$ 5 yields 0.2, find 17 $\boxed{y^x}$ 0.2. Therefore, $\sqrt[5]{17} \approx 1.76$. Use your exponent key to find the following to 2 decimal places.

_____    **5.** $\sqrt[4]{23}$        _____    **8.** $\sqrt[7]{502}$

_____    **6.** $106^{\frac{1}{2}}$        _____    **9.** $\sqrt[3]{311}$

_____    **7.** $79^{\frac{1}{10}}$        _____    **10.** $25^{\frac{1}{5}}$

The exponential method can be improved upon depending on your calculator. If you have a $\boxed{\sqrt[3]{\phantom{x}}}$ key for cube roots, you can use it like the square root key. Use the cube root key (or the exponential method if you don't have a cube root key) to find the following.

_____    **11.** $\sqrt[3]{483}$        _____    **13.** $\sqrt[3]{125}$

_____    **12.** $\sqrt[3]{5832}$        _____    **14.** $\sqrt[3]{7915}$

There is another key on your calculator that is used to find roots. Locate the radical key, $\boxed{\sqrt[x]{y}}$, on your calculator. Using it is very similar to using the exponent key. To find $\sqrt[4]{3.1}$, press these keys: 3.1 $\boxed{\sqrt[x]{y}}$ 4 $\boxed{=}$. The answer should be about 1.33. On many calculators this key is the inverse of the exponential key, so be sure to press $\boxed{\text{2nd}}$ or $\boxed{\text{INV}}$ if you need to. Of course, this method also works for square roots by entering 2 for the index, but the special square root key is faster. Calculate the following to 3 decimal places.

_____    **15.** $\sqrt[4]{101}$        _____    **23.** $\sqrt{100}$

_____    **16.** $\sqrt[5]{86}$        _____    **24.** $\sqrt[3]{100}$

_____    **17.** $\sqrt[12]{68}$        _____    **25.** $\sqrt[4]{100}$

_____    **18.** $\sqrt[7]{55}$        _____    **26.** $\sqrt[5]{100}$

_____    **19.** $\sqrt[21]{306}$        _____    **27.** $\sqrt[6]{100}$

_____    **20.** $\sqrt[56]{1000}$        _____    **28.** $\sqrt[10]{100}$

_____    **21.** $\sqrt[8]{408}$        _____    **29.** $\sqrt[25]{100}$

_____    **22.** $\sqrt[9]{8527}$        _____    **30.** $\sqrt[100]{100}$

**31.** Look at questions 23 to 30. What happens as you take higher roots of a

number? _____

**32.** Find $\sqrt[10{,}000]{100}$. _____

# Radicals in Brief

## PYTHAGOREAN TRIPLES

Certain triples of numbers in the natural number system have a special property used for studying right triangles. For example, the ordered triple $(2, 0, 2)$ and the ordered triple $(4, 3, 5)$, when put into $a^2 + b^2 = c^2$, reveal that the sum of the squares of the first two numbers is equal to the square of the third.

$$2^2 + 0^2 = 2^2 \qquad 4^2 + 3^2 = 5^2$$
$$4 + 0 = 4 \qquad 16 + 9 = 25$$
$$4 = 4 \qquad 25 = 25$$

1. Lines one and two in the table below are Pythagorean triples. Check that lines three and four are also Pythagorean triples.

|     | a | b | c |
|-----|---|---|----|
| (1) | 2 | 0 | 2 |
| (2) | 4 | 3 | 5 |
| (3) | 6 | 8 | 10 |
| (4) | 8 | 15 | 17 |

Notice that the numbers in the first column are two times the line number. The numbers in the middle column equal the line number squared less one. The numbers in the third column equal the line number squared plus one. For example, in the third line you can see that $a = 2 \cdot 3 = 6$, $b = 3^2 - 1 = 8$, and $c = 3^2 + 1 = 10$.

2. Following this method, find the seventh and ninth lines of triples.

|     |   |   |   |
|-----|---|---|---|
| (7) | ? | ? | ? |
| (9) | ? | ? | ? |

_____

_____

3. Finish the table of the first ten Pythagorean triples by calculating the 5th, 6th, 8th, and 10th rows.

|      | a | b | c |
|------|---|---|---|
| (5)  | ? | ? | ? |
| (6)  | ? | ? | ? |
| (8)  | ? | ? | ? |
| (10) | ? | ? | ? |

_____

_____

_____

_____

4. Examine rows 2 and 3 of the table. What do you notice about the third Pythagorean triple in relation to the second?

_____

_____

5. Is 9, 12, 15 a Pythagorean triple? Use the Pythagorean theorem to verify.

_____

6. How does this Pythagorean triple relate to the second row of the table?

_____

7. Draw a conclusion from your discovery. _____

_____

8. Will the formula given in this lesson produce all possible Pythagorean triples? _____

# Radicals Applied

## *TRIANGLES AND EQUATIONS*

**Find the length of the third side for each triangle.**

_____ **1.**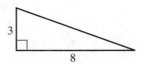

_____ **2.**

_____ **3.**

_____ **4.**

_____ **5.**

_____ **6.**

**Find the distance between the points.**

_____ **7.**

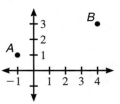

_____ **8.**

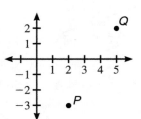

_____ **9.**

_____ **10.**

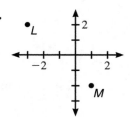

**Solve each radical equation.**

_____ **11.** $\sqrt{y} = 13$

_____ **12.** $2\sqrt{x} = 16$

_____ **13.** $\sqrt{x - 5} = 7$

_____ **14.** $\sqrt{x + 8} = 12$

_____ **15.** $\sqrt{3x - 5} = 7$

_____ **16.** $\sqrt{4x + 1} = 21$

_____ **17.** $5 + 3\sqrt{y} = 41$

_____ **18.** $14 - 2\sqrt{x + 8} = 8$

_____ **19.** $9 + \sqrt{x - 6} = 5$

_____ **20.** $11 - 5\sqrt{2x - 5} = -4$

**Simplify.**

_____ **21.** $\sqrt{2}(3 + \sqrt{5})$     _____ **24.** $\dfrac{\sqrt{3}}{5 + \sqrt{2}}$

_____ **22.** $(5 - \sqrt{2})(5 + \sqrt{2})$     _____ **25.** $(\sqrt{2} + \sqrt{3})^2$

_____ **23.** $\dfrac{5 + \sqrt{2}}{\sqrt{3}}$     _____ **26.** $\dfrac{\sqrt{5} + \sqrt{2}}{\sqrt{6} - \sqrt{3}}$

**27.** If the legs of a right triangle are 5 and 7 feet long respectively, find the

length of the hypotenuse. _____

**28.** Find the perimeter of the triangle in the graph.

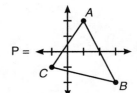

$P =$

_____

**29.** Five more than the square root of a number is fourteen. Find the number.

_____

**30.** A 100 ft. wire stretches from the top of a tower to a point on the ground
20 feet from the base of the tower. How high is the tower?

_____

# Radicals in Detail

## PYTHAGOREAN PROBLEMS

Radicals are needed in order to answer many practical questions regarding lengths, areas, and volumes. Solve for *x*.

_____ **1.**

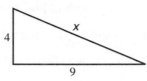

_____ **2.**

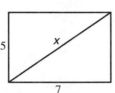

_____ **3.**

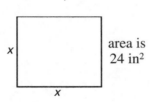

_____ **4.**

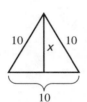

_____ **5.**

_____ **6.**

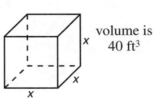

Solve each word problem.

**7.** A wooden ramp is to be constructed to span a three foot vertical drop. How long will the ramp be if it is to be anchored 12 feet from the drop?

_____

8. Mrs. Stone plans to plant a vegetable garden. The vegetables she wants to grow will require 216 square feet. What length should the sides measure for a square vegetable garden? _____

9. Mr. Farmwell has a fenced rectangular pen that measures 60 feet by 80 feet. He wishes to divide it into two pens by building a fence diagonally across the existing pen. How long should the new fence be? _____

10. A natural gas company needs a cubical tank able to hold 768 cubic feet of gas. How long should each side be? _____

# ■ Practice

## ESTIMATING RADICALS

**Identify the nearest integer.**

_____ **1.** $\sqrt{7}$          _____ **11.** $\sqrt{315}$

_____ **2.** $\sqrt{15}$         _____ **12.** $\sqrt{291}$

_____ **3.** $\sqrt{34}$         _____ **13.** $\sqrt{619}$

_____ **4.** $\sqrt{94}$         _____ **14.** $\sqrt{88}$

_____ **5.** $\sqrt{124}$        _____ **15.** $\sqrt{150}$

_____ **6.** $\sqrt{26}$         _____ **16.** $\sqrt{45}$

_____ **7.** $\sqrt{513}$        _____ **17.** $\sqrt{333}$

_____ **8.** $\sqrt{186}$        _____ **18.** $\sqrt{229}$

_____ **9.** $\sqrt{421}$        _____ **19.** $\sqrt{170}$

_____ **10.** $\sqrt{107}$       _____ **20.** $\sqrt{270}$

**Use > and < to compare the radical and fraction.**

_____ **21.** $\sqrt{2}$   $\frac{3}{2}$          _____ **26.** $\sqrt{80}$   $8\frac{1}{2}$

_____ **22.** $\sqrt{6}$   $\frac{5}{2}$          _____ **27.** $\sqrt{37}$   $6\frac{1}{3}$

_____ **23.** $\sqrt{12}$  $\frac{31}{10}$        _____ **28.** $\sqrt{44}$   $6\frac{1}{2}$

_____ **24.** $\sqrt{19}$  $\frac{13}{3}$         _____ **29.** $\sqrt{51}$   $7\frac{1}{5}$

_____ **25.** $\sqrt{28}$  $5\frac{2}{5}$         _____ **30.** $\sqrt{66}$   $8\frac{1}{4}$

**Estimate to the nearest tenth.**

_____ **31.** $\sqrt{53}$        _____ **36.** $\sqrt{159}$

_____ **32.** $\sqrt{8}$         _____ **37.** $\sqrt{40}$

_____ **33.** $\sqrt{17}$        _____ **38.** $\sqrt{2}$

_____ **34.** $\sqrt{67}$        _____ **39.** $\sqrt{114}$

_____ **35.** $\sqrt{29}$        _____ **40.** $\sqrt{285}$

# ■ Practice

### SIMPLIFYING RADICALS

**Approximate each radical to the nearest tenth using a table of square roots or successive approximations.**

| | |
|---|---|
| **1.** $\sqrt{78}$ | **6.** $\sqrt{548}$ |
| **2.** $\sqrt{11}$ | **7.** $\sqrt{441}$ |
| **3.** $\sqrt{53}$ | **8.** $\sqrt{234}$ |
| **4.** $\sqrt{208}$ | **9.** $\sqrt{289}$ |
| **5.** $\sqrt{69}$ | **10.** $\sqrt{401}$ |

**Simplify by writing each expression involving exponents in radical form.**

| | |
|---|---|
| **11.** $14^{\frac{1}{19}}$ | **16.** $3^{\frac{1}{4}}x^{\frac{1}{2}}$ |
| **12.** $7^{\frac{5}{6}}$ | **17.** $7^{\frac{3}{5}}y^{\frac{1}{10}}$ |
| **13.** $x^{\frac{2}{3}}$ | **18.** $4^{\frac{3}{8}}x^{\frac{1}{4}}y^{\frac{5}{8}}z^{\frac{1}{8}}$ |
| **14.** $2^{\frac{1}{7}}z^{\frac{1}{7}}$ | **19.** $11^{\frac{1}{2}}x^{\frac{1}{3}}$ |
| **15.** $5^{\frac{2}{3}}x^{\frac{1}{3}}y^{\frac{2}{3}}$ | **20.** $x^{-\frac{3}{5}}$ |

**Simplify.**

| | |
|---|---|
| **21.** $\sqrt{180}$ | **26.** $\sqrt[3]{189}$ |
| **22.** $\sqrt{75}$ | **27.** $\sqrt{52}$ |
| **23.** $\sqrt[3]{384}$ | **28.** $\sqrt{140}$ |
| **24.** $\sqrt[4]{324}$ | **29.** $\sqrt[3]{343}$ |
| **25.** $\sqrt[5]{48}$ | **30.** $\sqrt[4]{80}$ |

# ■ Practice

### OPERATIONS WITH RADICALS

**Multiply.**

_____ 1. $\sqrt{15} \cdot \sqrt{3}$    _____ 6. $\sqrt[4]{18} \cdot \sqrt[4]{24}$

_____ 2. $\sqrt{11} \cdot \sqrt{2}$    _____ 7. $\sqrt{3xy} \cdot \sqrt{6y}$

_____ 3. $\sqrt{6} \cdot \sqrt{8}$    _____ 8. $\sqrt{32} \cdot \sqrt{3}$

_____ 4. $\sqrt{70} \cdot \sqrt{21}$    _____ 9. $\sqrt{7x^3y} \cdot \sqrt{4x^2y}$

_____ 5. $\sqrt[3]{20} \cdot \sqrt[3]{10}$    _____ 10. $\sqrt[4]{x^3yz^5} \cdot \sqrt[4]{2xy^2z}$

**Divide.**

_____ 11. $\dfrac{6}{\sqrt{2}}$    _____ 16. $\sqrt[3]{11} \div \sqrt[3]{2}$

_____ 12. $\dfrac{11\sqrt{7}}{\sqrt{3}}$    _____ 17. $\sqrt{10xy} \div \sqrt{5xy^2}$

_____ 13. $\sqrt{7} \div \sqrt{28}$    _____ 18. $\dfrac{5}{\sqrt[3]{49}}$

_____ 14. $\sqrt{16} \div \sqrt{6}$    _____ 19. $\dfrac{\sqrt{50x^3y}}{\sqrt{8x^4y}}$

_____ 15. $\dfrac{\sqrt[3]{80}}{\sqrt[3]{10}}$    _____ 20. $\dfrac{\sqrt[3]{9x^3y^2z^5}}{\sqrt[3]{9x^4y^4z}}$

**Add or subtract.**

_____ 21. $\sqrt{23} - 5\sqrt{23}$

_____ 22. $19\sqrt{37} - 11\sqrt{37}$

_____ 23. $10\sqrt{7} + \sqrt{28}$

_____ 24. $8\sqrt{44} + 5\sqrt{44}$

_____ 25. $x\sqrt{5} - 2x\sqrt{5}$

_____ 26. $17\sqrt{y} - 15\sqrt{4y}$

_____ 27. $\sqrt{200} + \sqrt{98}$

_____ 28. $3\sqrt{10} - \sqrt{6} - \sqrt{90}$

_____ 29. $\sqrt{x^2y} + 5x\sqrt{y} - x\sqrt{9y}$

_____ 30. $4\sqrt{3x} - 2\sqrt{27x} + \sqrt{18x}$

**Simplify.**

_____ **31.** $\sqrt{5} \cdot \sqrt{10}$

_____ **32.** $\sqrt{7} \div \sqrt{45}$

_____ **33.** $\sqrt{36x} - \sqrt{121x}$

_____ **34.** $\dfrac{4}{\sqrt[3]{y^2}}$

_____ **35.** $\sqrt[4]{12x^5y} \cdot \sqrt[4]{8xy^4}$

_____ **36.** $\sqrt{63} + \sqrt{112}$

_____ **37.** $\dfrac{3\sqrt{120}}{\sqrt{63}}$

_____ **38.** $\sqrt[5]{2x} \cdot \sqrt[5]{8xy}$

_____ **39.** $x\sqrt{54x} - 3\sqrt{6x^3}$

_____ **40.** $\sqrt[3]{9xy^2} \div \sqrt[3]{4xz}$

# ■ Cumulative Review

**Graph.**

1. $-\sqrt{5}$

2. $2 - x \geq 7$

3. $y = -3x + 2$

4. $\{(x, y) \mid x = 2 \text{ and } 1 < y < 3\}$

5. $4x - 3y > 6$

Cumulative Review

**Solve.**

_____  **6.** $2(x + 5) + 4x = 7$

_____  **7.** $|5x + 2| \geq 4$

_____  **8.** $\frac{x}{12} - \frac{5}{28} = x - \frac{2}{21}$

_____  **9.** $\sqrt{x - 3} = 6$

_____  **10.** $\begin{matrix} x - y = 17 \\ x + y = 35 \end{matrix}$

**Factor.**

_____  **11.** $x^2 - 5x - 24$

_____  **12.** $6x^2 - 54$

_____  **13.** $6x^2 + 7x - 20$

_____  **14.** $8x^3 - 8x^2 + 2x$

**Give the nearest whole numbers.**

_____  **15.** $\sqrt{29}$

_____  **16.** $\sqrt[3]{37}$

**Classify the kind**

_____  **17.** of number: $\sqrt{3}$

_____  **18.** of polynomial: $x^8 - 5x^3 + 7$

**Use (2, −6) and (5, 3) to find**

_____  **19.** the slope of the line.

_____  **20.** the distance between the points.

**Evaluate if $x = -3$ and $y = 12$.**

_____  **21.** $2x^2 + x$

_____  **22.** $Q = \frac{y}{x}$

**Perform the indicated operation.**

_____ **23.** $x > -2 \wedge x < 3$

_____ **24.** $\{2,3,5,7,11\} \cup \{1, 2, 3, 5, 8, 13\}$

_____ **25.** How many solutions does an inconsistent system have?

**Simplify.**

_____ **26.** $\frac{1}{5} - \frac{2}{7}$

_____ **27.** $|-6|$

_____ **28.** $\sqrt{20} - 7\sqrt{5}$

_____ **29.** $5 - 6 \cdot 3 \div 2 + 2$

_____ **30.** $(-5)(-7)$

_____ **31.** $(x + 3)(x - 2)$

_____ **32.** $(-2)^5$

_____ **33.** $\frac{4x^5 - 14x^3 + 10x^2}{2x^2}$

_____ **34.** $\frac{\sqrt{8xy}}{\sqrt{3x^2y}}$

_____ **35.** $(5x^2y + 7x - 8y) - (2x^2y + 3x - 2xy^2)$

**Translate each phrase into symbols.**

_____ **36.** seven less than twice a number

_____ **37.** the quotient of a number and 3 more than the number

**Solve these word problems.**

**38.** A telephone pole is 18 ft. high. A cable is anchored to the ground 10 ft. from the base of the pole. How long must the cable be?

_____

**39.** Jeff has 40 coins with a total value of $5.35 in nickels, dimes, and quarters. How many of each are there if there are 5 more quarters than nickels?

_____

**40.** Write from memory Judges 7:16.

_____

_____

_____

# CHAPTER 11
## Quadratic Equations

## Bible: Subtraction

Subtraction occurs twice in the quadratic formula. Do you know where? Subtraction occurs in the Bible in a literal sense in I Kings 6:37-38 and Genesis 18:28.

**The literal sense of subtraction involves the idea of reduction, decrease, removal, or taking away. Each of the following passages uses various terms related to subtraction in a nonmathematical sense. Identify the term related to the operation of subtraction in each passage.**

    **1.** I Kings 14:26 _____

    **2.** Psalm 107:38 _____

    **3.** Judges 21:3 _____

    **4.** Ezra 9:13 _____

    **5.** Mark 4:15 _____

    **6.** II Kings 18:4 _____

    **7.** Exodus 11:7 _____

    **8.** Leviticus 25:16 _____

    **9.** Ephesians 4:25 _____

    **10.** Proverbs 10:27 _____

**Identify the subtrahend in each passage. The subtrahend is the object being subtracted. Also, give the word or phrase indicating subtraction.**

    **11.** II Samuel 2:30 _____

    **12.** John 1:29 _____

    **13.** John 20:1 _____

    **14.** I Kings 15:12*b* _____

    **15.** Luke 8:12 _____

**Identify the minuend in each passage. The minuend is the object that is taken from or diminished. Also, give the word or phrase that indicates subtraction.**

16. II Samuel 2:30 _____

17. John 3:30 _____

18. Revelation 22:19 _____

_____

19. John 20:1 _____

20. Review the memory verse Genesis 18:28. Identify the operational word, subtrahend, and minuend. _____

# Math History: Diophantus

### SOLVING QUADRATIC EQUATIONS

The Greek mathematician Diophantus used quadratic equations and symbols to solve problems. Diophantus solved quadratic equations using a method similar to the completing the square method.

1. When did Diophantus live? _____

2. Where did he live? _____

3. What was his most important book? _____

4. The book made some significant contributions to math. What does the book discuss?

   _____

5. He was the first to solve equations in symbolic form. How had algebra

   been done previously? _____

6. He also changed the approach to solving equations. Practical mathematics, such as in Babylon, sought for approximate solutions. What did

   Diophantus seek? _____

7. Did he discuss properties like the commutative law in his book? _____

   Even though he used symbols, you should not think his methods are abstract. He solves about 150 problems, but he does not attempt to find all possible answers to his equations.

8. Though his goals were not abstract, his numbers were. How are the Egyptian and Babylonian problems different from Diophantus's?

   _____

   _____

9. Because of the advances he made in symbolism, using abstract numbers and seeking better than approximate solutions, some people consider

   Diophantus to be the Father of _____

10. Two other works are referred to in *Arithmetica*. What are they about?

    _____

## *Calculator Skills*

### MISCELLANEOUS KEYS

This chapter on quadratics provides another opportunity to study powers on your calculator.

You have already learned how to square, square root, cube, cube root, x-power ($y^x$), and x-root ($\sqrt[x]{y}$). In this activity you will expand your usage of these keys and learn to use two other keys related to exponents.

**Compare. (*Hint:* If you subtract, the sign will tell you which is bigger. What will you get if they are equal?)**

1. $10^{0.5}$ using the power key with $\sqrt{10}$ using the root key. _____

2. $7^{0.1}$ using power key, $y^x$ with $\sqrt[10]{7}$ using the root key. _____

**Now find each of the following using only the $y^x$ key. Carry four decimal places.**

_____ 3. $5^{2.31679}$      _____ 6. $4^{\pi}$

_____ 4. $\sqrt[3]{4}$      _____ 7. $\pi^{\sqrt{5}}$

_____ 5. $3^{-5}$      _____ 8. $(11.31)^{\sqrt[5]{7}}$

9. Now look for the $\boxed{10^x}$ key. Find $10^{0.5}$ by entering 0.5 $\boxed{10^x}$. Did you get the same result as in question 1? _____

10. Of course you can use this key only for powers of ten. Another special key is the $\boxed{e^x}$ key. It is important to know that $e$ is a special number like $\pi$. It is irrational. Find its approximate value by entering $e^1$ (1 $\boxed{e^x}$).

**Find the following values using the easiest method on your calculator. Round to four decimal places.**

_____ **11.** $\sqrt{e}$

_____ **12.** $10^{\sqrt[3]{5}}$

_____ **13.** $\dfrac{1}{\sqrt[3]{10^2}}$

_____ **14.** $\left(\sqrt{7}\right)^{\sqrt{5}}$

_____ **15.** $\left(\dfrac{8}{3}\right)^{\pi+1}$

_____ **16.** $10^e - e^{10}$

_____ **17.** $e^{\pi^2} - \left(e^{\pi}\right)^2$

_____ **18.** $\left(\sqrt[11]{935}\right)^2$

_____ **19.** $(\pi - e)^2$

_____ **20.** $10^{-\frac{5}{6}}$

Base $e$ is very important since the function $f(x) = \dfrac{1}{\sqrt{2\pi}} e^{-\frac{1}{2}x^2}$ describes the standard normal curve (bell-shaped).

**Find the following values using the function $f(x)$ above to four decimal places.**

_____ **21.** $f(0)$

_____ **22.** $f(1)$

_____ **23.** $f(2)$

_____ **24.** $f(3)$

**25.** Graph the standard normal function using the points you found.

# Graphing in Brief: Summary

I. Number lines

    A. No variables

        1. Integer

        2. Fraction            —approximate as decimal

        3. Radical             —approximate as decimal

        4. Set of numbers     — graph each number in set

    B. One variable

        1. Equation        —solve it, then graph the solution

           a. Linear        —usually one solution (sometimes none)

           b. Absolute values   —usually two solutions (sometimes less)

           c. Quadratic      —usually two solutions (sometimes less)

           d. Radical         —usually one solution (sometimes none)

        2. Inequalities      —solve it, then graph the solution

           a. simple (linear)    —a ray (with or without an endpoint)

           b. compound

               1) conjunction, $\wedge$, "and"   —segmented usually like $|Ax + B| \leq C$

               2) disjunction, $\vee$, "or"    —two rays usually like $|Ax + B| \geq C$

II. Cartesian Plane

    A. No variables

        1. Ordered pair (x, y)

        2. Set of ordered pairs   —plot each point

    B. One variable

    (These should be graphed on number lines unless context or instructions require the plane.)

        1. Equation

           a. $x = a$          —vertical line

           b. $y = b$          —horizontal line

        2. Inequality

           a. involving $x$    —shade right or left of vertical line (dotted if needed)

           b. involving $y$    —shade above or below horizontal line (dotted if needed)

    C. Two variables

        1. Equations

           a. Lines $y = mx + b$ —use $y$-intercept $b$ and slope $m$

           b. Otherwise, plot points until you see the pattern.

              Note: in Chapter 14 you will learn parabolas: $y = a(x - h)^2 + k$

           c. Systems       —graph both on same plane

        2. Inequalities

           a. One         —graph equality, make it dotted if needed, shade correct side

           b. Two         —graph both inequalities, shade where they overlap

# Graphing Review

## DECISION TREE

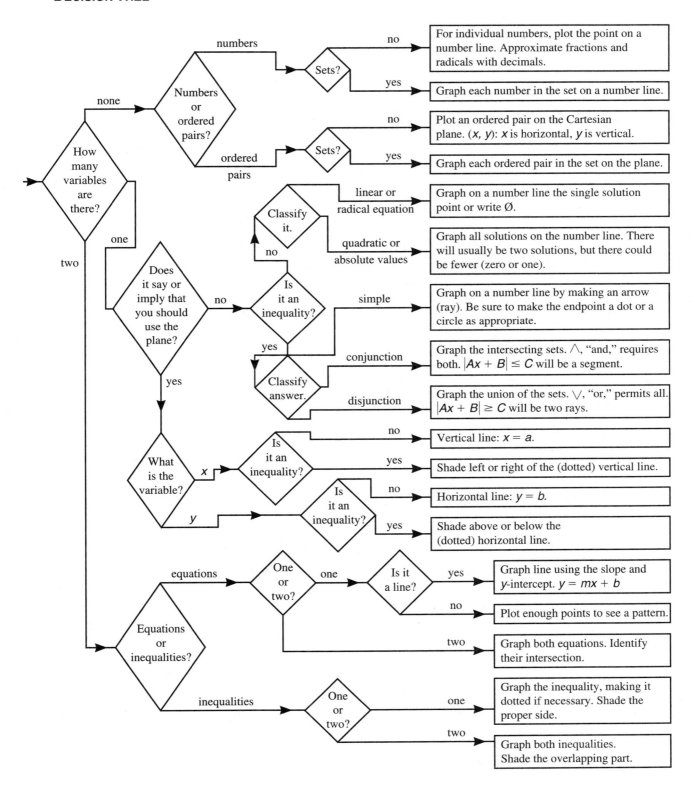

# Graphing Review

**Graph:**

    **1.** $x < 5$

    **2.** $(-3, -2)$

    **3.** $7x + 3 = -25$

    **4.** $x > 3$ and $x \leq 5$

    **5.** $y = \frac{2}{3}x - 1$

    **6.** $\{(x, y) \mid y = |1 - x| \text{ for } x = -1, 0, 1, 2, 3, 4\}$

    **7.** $-\frac{11}{4}$

**8.** $2x + 5y > 20$

**9.** $|x - 2| > 3$

**10.** $\{(x, y) \mid x = 2\}$

**11.** $6 = x^2 - 3$

**12.** $y = x^2 - 3$

**13.** $3x + 5 = 3x - 7$

**14.** $2x^2 - 5x + 8 = x(x + 1)$

**15.** $3x - 4y = 8$
$2x - y = 7$

**16.** $3\sqrt{x} + 7 = 13$

**17.** $-\sqrt{11}$

**18.** $3x + y \leq 2$
$y \geq 3$

**19.** $\sqrt{3x + 5} = -1$

**20.** $y = -3(x - 2)^2 + 5$

# Quadratics Applied: Circles

The following problems are very similar to the word problems involving areas of rectangles. The primary difference is that they involve circles. If you draw a picture and remember the formulas $C = 2\pi r$ and $A = \pi r^2$ for circumference and area, you should be able to do them. You may leave $\pi$ in your answers or use your calculator and give the answer to three decimal places.

1. If five more than the circumference of a circle is 27, then find the radius.

   _____

2. If seven less than the area of a circle is 63, then find the radius.

   _____

3. If the area of a circle is $11\pi$, then find the radius. _____

4. Find the radius of a circle which has an area equal to its circumference.

   _____

5. The area of a circle is six times the circumference. Find the radius of the

   circle. _____

6. The area of a circle is $15\pi$ more than the circumference. Find the radius.

   _____

7. The sum of the circumference and the area is $63\pi$. Find the radius. _____

8. If the radius of a circle is decreased by 2 inches, the area will be 50 sq.

   inches. Find the radius. _____

9. Mr. Grady has a circular plot of 113 sq. yds. He intends to put in a sidewalk around the edge but inside the circle. How wide should it be if the remaining flower bed will have a radius of 4.2 yards?

   _____

10. Three less than the area of a circle is numerically the same as the radius.

    Find the radius. _____

# Equations in Detail: Polynomial and Radical Equations

So far you have learned several methods for solving quadratic equations. Both factoring and taking roots apply to higher powers also. Remember to use $\sqrt[n]{\phantom{x}}$ to undo $x^n$. Simplify radicals if possible.

1. $x^3 = 1$
2. $x^3 = -64$
3. $x^3 = 40$
4. $x^4 = 81$
5. $x^5 = 64$
6. $x^3 + 54 = 0$
7. $2x^5 + 5 = 3$
8. $x^3 + 2x^2 + x = 0$
9. $x^3 - 5x^2 - 24x = 0$
10. $4x^3 + 10x = 10x - 32$
11. $x^4 - 16x^2 + 64 = 0$
12. $6x^3 + 13x^2 - 28x = 0$
13. $x^4 + x^3 - 2x - 2 = 0$
14. $2x^5 - 3x^3 + 5 = x^4 + 5$

You also learned how to solve radical equations. Use the same principles to solve these radical equations. You will have to do $n$th powers to undo the $n$th-roots. You need to check only even-indexed equations.

15. $\sqrt[3]{x} = 7$
16. $\sqrt[3]{x} = 5$
17. $\sqrt[4]{x} = 4$
18. $\sqrt[3]{x + 1} = 3$
19. $\sqrt[5]{x - 9} = 2$
20. $3 - 2\sqrt[3]{x} = 15$
21. $\sqrt[8]{2x + 3} = \sqrt[8]{x^2}$
22. $\sqrt[3]{x^2 - 3x - 2} = 2$
23. $\sqrt[5]{x^2 - 5} = -1$
24. $\sqrt[7]{x^2 + 3} = \sqrt[7]{4x + 3}$
25. $11 - 2\sqrt[3]{3x^2 - 20x + 20} = 5$

Finally, study both solutions to this cube root problem.

$$\sqrt[3]{x^2} + 5\sqrt[3]{x} + 4 = 0$$
$$\left(\sqrt[3]{x} + 4\right)\left(\sqrt[3]{x} + 1\right) = 0$$
$$\sqrt[3]{x} + 4 = 0 \quad \text{or} \quad \sqrt[3]{x} + 1 = 0$$
$$\sqrt[3]{x} = -4 \quad \text{or} \quad \sqrt[3]{x} = -1$$
$$x = -64 \quad \text{or} \quad x = -1$$

$$\sqrt[3]{x^2} + 5\sqrt[3]{x} + 4 = 0$$
$$1\left(\sqrt[3]{x}\right)^2 + 5\left(\sqrt[3]{x}\right) + 4 = 0$$
$$\sqrt[3]{x} = \frac{-5 \pm \sqrt{25 - 4 \cdot 1 \cdot 4}}{2 \cdot 1}$$
$$\sqrt[3]{x} = \frac{-5 \pm \sqrt{9}}{2} = \frac{-5 \pm 3}{2}$$
$$\sqrt[3]{x} = \frac{-2}{2} = -1 \text{ or } \sqrt[3]{x} = \frac{-8}{2} = -4$$
$$x = -1 \quad \text{or} \quad x = -64$$

**Use the factoring or quadratic formula methods illustrated to solve these radical equations.**

26. $\sqrt[3]{x^2} - 10\sqrt[3]{x} + 21 = 0$ _____

27. $\sqrt[3]{x^2} + 4\sqrt[3]{x} + 2 = 0$ _____

28. $2\sqrt[3]{x^2} - \sqrt[3]{x} - 6 = 0$ _____

29. $\sqrt[3]{x^2} - 3 = 4\sqrt[3]{x}$ _____

30. $1 + \sqrt[3]{x} = \sqrt[3]{x + 7}$ (*Hint:* Cube both sides.) _____

# ■ Practice ·······························································································

## SOLVING QUADRATICS BY FACTORING

**Use the zero product property to solve each equation.**

_____ **1.** $(x - 5)(x + 8) = 0$          _____ **6.** $(x - 11)(x - 29) = 0$

_____ **2.** $(x + 12)(x - 17) = 0$          _____ **7.** $6x(x + 10) = 0$

_____ **3.** $(x - 9)(x - 8) = 0$          _____ **8.** $(x + 4)(2x - 1) = 0$

_____ **4.** $(x - 51)(x + 51) = 0$          _____ **9.** $2x(3x + 7)(x - 6) = 0$

_____ **5.** $(x + 10)(x + 13) = 0$          _____ **10.** $13x(x + 80) = 0$

**Solve each equation by factoring.**

_____ **11.** $x^2 - 1 = 0$          _____ **16.** $2x^2 + 11x + 12 = 0$

_____ **12.** $x^2 + 3x - 4 = 0$          _____ **17.** $16x^2 = 25$

_____ **13.** $x^2 - 3x - 40 = 0$          _____ **18.** $9x^2 + 4 = 12x$

_____ **14.** $100x^2 - 49 = 0$          _____ **19.** $5 + 34x = 7x^2$

_____ **15.** $x^2 + 10x + 25 = 0$          _____ **20.** $12x^2 - 13x = 14$

**Solve each equation below.**

_____ **21.** $5x^2 - 17x - 12 = 0$

_____ **22.** $28 + x^2 - 11x = 0$

_____ **23.** $x^2 + 3x = 0$

_____ **24.** $11x(x - 6) = 0$

_____ **25.** $4x^2 + 4x + 1 = 0$

_____ **26.** $4x^2 - 9 = 0$

_____ **27.** $8x^2 + 12x = 0$

_____ **28.** $33x(x + 4)(3x - 1) = 0$

_____ **29.** $15x^2 + 3x = x + 24$

_____ **30.** $3 - 2x = x^2$

# ■ Practice ················································

## TAKING ROOTS AND COMPLETING THE SQUARE

**Solve each equation by taking the root.**

_____ **1.** $x^2 = 16$     _____ **6.** $2x^2 + 3 = 59$

_____ **2.** $x^2 = 3$     _____ **7.** $x^2 + 8 = 19$

_____ **3.** $x^2 - 25 = 0$     _____ **8.** $(x - 1)^2 = 27$

_____ **4.** $x^2 - 13 = 0$     _____ **9.** $4x^2 - 8 = x^2 + 28$

_____ **5.** $3x^2 - 7 = 11$     _____ **10.** $(x - 3)^2 = 81$

**Solve each equation by completing the square.**

_____ **11.** $x^2 - 4x = 5$

_____ **12.** $x^2 - 14x + 33 = 0$

_____ **13.** $x^2 + 10x - 24 = 0$

_____ **14.** $x^2 + 2x = 35$

_____ **15.** $x^2 + 20x + 91 = 0$

_____ **16.** $x^2 + 3x = 7$

_____ **17.** $6x^2 - 13x - 5 = 0$

_____ **18.** $3x^2 + 6x = 60$

_____ **19.** $2x^2 + 3x = 0$

_____ **20.** $5x^2 + 7x - 3 = 0$

**Solve each quadratic equation by the easiest method.**

_____ **21.** $2x^2 = 80$

_____ **22.** $x^2 + 8x = 7$

_____ **23.** $6x^2 - 26x - 20 = 0$

_____ **24.** $9x^2 = 7$

_____ **25.** $2x^2 - 5x - 4 = 0$

# ■ Practice ·····································································

### THE QUADRATIC FORMULA

**Solve using the quadratic formula.**

_____ **1.** $x^2 + x - 1 = 0$      _____ **6.** $x^2 - 9x + 2 = 0$

_____ **2.** $x^2 + 3x + 2 = 0$      _____ **7.** $6x - 3 = x^2$

_____ **3.** $x^2 + 4x = -4$      _____ **8.** $2x^2 + 10 = 9x$

_____ **4.** $2x^2 + 4 = 7x$      _____ **9.** $4x^2 - 2x - 3 = 0$

_____ **5.** $3x^2 + 8x = 4$      _____ **10.** $2x^2 = 5 - x$

**Solve using any method.**

_____ **11.** $x^2 + 5x + 2 = 0$

_____ **12.** $x^2 + 3x + 7 = 0$

_____ **13.** $2x^2 - 450 = 0$

_____ **14.** $4x^2 + 7x + 3 = 0$

_____ **15.** $9x^2 - 12x + 4 = 0$

_____ **16.** $8x + 9 + x^2 = 0$

_____ **17.** $4x^2 + x + 3 = 0$

_____ **18.** $x^2 + 1 = 65$

_____ **19.** $4x^2 + 25 = 20x$

_____ **20.** $x^2 - 3x = 6$

# ■ Cumulative Review ...........................................................

**Match to each equation the number and nature of its solutions. Letters may be used more than once or not at all.**

_____ **1.** $|5x - 8| = -3$

_____ **2.** $5x - 2 = 3y$
$\qquad 10x - 6y = 4$

_____ **3.** $x^2 + x + 1 = 0$

_____ **4.** $x^2 + 5x + 1 = 0$

_____ **5.** $x^2 + 2x + 1 = 0$

_____ **6.** $12x + 3y = 7$
$\qquad 28x + 7y = 16$

_____ **7.** $5x^2 - 8 = -3$

_____ **8.** $\sqrt{5x - 8} + 3 = 0$

_____ **9.** $5x - 8 = -3$

_____ **10.** $x^2 + y = 5$
$\qquad y = x$

**A.** infinitely many ordered pairs
**B.** two ordered pairs
**C.** one ordered pair
**D.** no solutions
**E.** one real number (rational)
**F.** two real numbers (rational)
**G.** two real numbers (irrational)
**H.** two complex numbers

**Solve.**

_____ **11.** $|x + 5| = 11$

_____ **12.** $3x - 5 = 13$

_____ **13.** $\sqrt{5x + 4} = 13$

_____ **14.** $x^2 + 7x + 12 = 0$

_____ **15.** $7x + 3(x - 5) = 2(3 - x)$

_____ **16.** $5x - 3 < 2 \text{ or } 3x + 1 > 4$

_____ **17.** $\frac{x}{5} + \frac{3}{20} = \frac{x}{10} - \frac{5}{6}$

_____ **18.** $|3x - 5| < 4$

_____ **19.** $2x^2 - 3x - 4 = 0$

_____ **20.** $2x - y = 4$
$\qquad 3x + y = 5$

**Simplify.**

21. $7x^2y - 8x(x - y) + 5x^2 - 2x$ _____

22. $(5 + 2x)(3 - x)$ _____

23. $\sqrt{14}(\sqrt{7} - \sqrt{2} + 2\sqrt{6})$ _____

24. $\dfrac{7x^3y^2 - 3x^2y^2 + 5x^2y}{x^2y}$ _____

25. $\dfrac{\sqrt{5} - \sqrt{3}}{\sqrt{5} + \sqrt{2}}$ _____

26. $\sqrt{48}$ _____

27. $\dfrac{18}{-12}$ _____

28. $\dfrac{5}{\sqrt{3}}$ _____

29. $(x^2 + 8x - 3) - (x^2 + 5x + 7)$ _____

30. $5^{-1}$ _____

**Graph on a number line.**

31. $\dfrac{5}{2}$

32. $x < 5$

33. $x \le 2$ and $x > -1$

**Graph on the Cartesian plane.**

34. $y = \dfrac{-2}{3}x + 5$

**35.** $y \geq 3$

**Factor.**

_____ **36.** $4x^2 - 1$  _____ **38.** $x^2 + 9x - 22$

_____ **37.** $6x^3 - 5x$  _____ **39.** $6x^2 - 7x - 24$

**40.** Write from memory:
   **a.** II Corinthians 5:21  **d.** Matthew 6:33
   **b.** Genesis 1:28  **e.** Genesis 18:28
   **c.** Judges 7:16

   **a.** _____

   _____

   _____

   **b.** _____

   _____

   _____

   _____

   _____

   **c.** _____

   _____

   _____

   **d.** _____

   _____

   _____

**e.** _____

_____

_____

_____

# CHAPTER 12
## Rational Expressions

## Bible: Multiples

Earlier you discovered that every book of the Bible contains numbers (if you include words for zero). You also found that all the whole numbers up through 42 appear in the Bible.

Find a verse in each book that contains the given multiples of five or ten. Remember that a score is twenty.

1. _____ 45 Joshua

2. _____ 50 II Kings

3. _____ 55 II Chronicles

4. _____ 60 I Timothy

5. _____ 65 Genesis

6. _____ 70 Genesis

7. _____ 75 Genesis

8. _____ 80 Psalms

9. _____ 85 Joshua

10. _____ 90 Genesis

11. _____ 95 Ezra

12. _____ 100 Genesis

13. _____ 105 Genesis

What multiples of ten can you find in these verses?

14. _____ Genesis 5:3

15. _____ Genesis 6:3

16. _____ Genesis 7:24

17. _____ Genesis 50:22

18. _____ Ezra 8:10

19. _____ Esther 1:4

20. _____ Job 42:16

What multiples of 50 or 100 can you find in these passages?

| | | | |
|---|---|---|---|
| **21.** _____ | Genesis 5:4 | **29.** _____ | II Chronicles 3:8 |
| **22.** _____ | Genesis 5:32 | **30.** _____ | II Chronicles 4:13 |
| **23.** _____ | Genesis 9:28 | **31.** _____ | II Chronicles 8:10 |
| **24.** _____ | Genesis 9:29 | **32.** _____ | II Chronicles 8:18 |
| **25.** _____ | Judges 4:3 | **33.** _____ | II Chronicles 9:16 |
| **26.** _____ | Judges 16:5 | **34.** _____ | II Chronicles 12:3 |
| **27.** _____ | I Kings 9:23 | **35.** _____ | II Chronicles 15:11 |
| **28.** _____ | I Chronicles 15:8 | **36.** _____ | Ezra 8:26 |
| | | **37.** _____ | Song of Solomon 8:11 |

The lowest whole number not found in the Bible is 43. Above, you found each multiple of five, ten, fifty, and one hundred up to the first one that does not occur in Scripture. Answer the following using your work above.

**38.** What is the lowest multiple of five that is not in the Bible? _____

**39.** Which multiples of ten smaller than 200 do not occur in the Bible?

_____

**40.** What is the lowest multiple of one hundred that is not in the Bible? _____

**41.** You have seen how important multiples of ten are in the Bible. Review the memory verse Leviticus 6:20 and give the power of ten referred to

in it. _____

## Math History: Tartaglia

Niccolo Tartaglia did considerable work with equations including fractions. Answer the questions about this mathematician.

1. When did he live? _____

2. What was his real name? _____

3. Why was he called Tartaglia? _____

   _____

   _____

4. Where was he from? _____

5. Who won the contest between Antonio Maria Fior and Tartaglia?

   _____

6. How did he win? _____

   _____

7. Which great mathematician became interested in Tartaglia as a result of

   the contest? _____

8. Though in violation of his trust, Cardan published Tartaglia's solution to the cubic equation in 1545 in *Artis magnae*. Under what title did Tartaglia publish his own results on cubics?

   _____

9. When did he publish them? _____

10. Tartaglia's first book, *Nova Scienza* (1537), dealt with what topic?

    _____

His later works on arithmetic (1556) and numbers (1560) were combined in *Trattato de numeri e misuri*. These works include an emphasis on practical word problems from business. Tartaglia also appears to have been the first to use parentheses in evaluating expressions.

## *Calculator Skills*

### RECIPROCALS

You have learned how to use your calculator different ways to find $\frac{973}{22^2 + 134}$. Review them.

1.  Scratch paper method (Chapter 1): calculate $22^2 + 134$, write it on scratch paper, and then divide 973 by the sum.

2.  Parentheses method (Chapter 2): calculate $973 \div (22^2 + 134)$.

3.  Memory method (Chapter 3): calculate $22^2 + 134$, save it in memory, and then divide 973 by $\boxed{\text{MR}}$.

4.  Memory/display switch method (Chapter 5): place 973 in memory, calculate $22^2 + 134$, and enter $\boxed{\text{X↔M}}$ $\boxed{\div}$ $\boxed{\text{MR}}$ $\boxed{=}$.

Now that you have more experience with fractions, you can learn a fifth method. It will use the reciprocal key $\boxed{\frac{1}{x}}$. The $\boxed{\text{2nd}}$ key may be needed.

Calculate the reciprocal of 2 by entering 2 $\boxed{\frac{1}{x}}$.

Your answer should be $\frac{1}{2}$ or 0.5. Reciprocals can be used to do division. You know that $70 \div 7 = 10$. Compute $\frac{70}{7}$ by using the reciprocal of 7. Enter 7 $\boxed{\frac{1}{x}}$ $\boxed{\times}$ 70 $\boxed{=}$. This works because dividing by 7 is the same as multiplying by $\frac{1}{7}$: $\frac{70}{7} = 70\left(\frac{1}{7}\right)$

5.  Reciprocal method: Calculate the reciprocal of $22^2 + 134$ (22 $\boxed{x^2}$ $\boxed{+}$ 134 $\boxed{=}$ $\boxed{\frac{1}{x}}$), and multiply by 973.

**Do the following calculations to three decimal places by evaluating the denominator first and then using the reciprocal method to divide.**

1. $\dfrac{35}{4 + 7 \cdot 13 - 6}$

2. $\dfrac{43.4}{12.5 - (3.6)(4.9)}$

3. $\dfrac{-56.4}{-22.4 + 9.2^2}$

4. $\dfrac{14.4}{\sqrt{8.91} - 4.3}$

5. $\dfrac{\sqrt{11.4}}{(3.9)^5 - (5.6)^2}$

6. $\dfrac{304.7}{\sqrt{77.3} - \sqrt{15.6}}$

7. $\dfrac{-35.8}{\sqrt[3]{53} + 2.3(7)}$

8. $\dfrac{0.35}{(1.4)^7 - \sqrt[7]{1.4}}$

9. $\dfrac{(2.33)^2}{4 - \left(\sqrt[5]{57}\right)^2}$

10. $\dfrac{(5.3)(16.4)}{9.2 + \sqrt[3]{11.2^2} + 3}$

**Use any methods you wish to evaluate these problems.**

_____  **11.** $89.6 + \dfrac{1}{(5.3)(4.7) - 53.4} - (3.4)(4.5)$

_____  **12.** $\dfrac{(2.8)^2 - 1}{(23.9)^2 + 5.6}$

_____  **13.** $\dfrac{3.5}{\sqrt{11.4 + 3.1}} + 89.9$

_____  **14.** $\sqrt[3]{\dfrac{257.4}{(13.6)^2 - (4.9)(71)}}$

_____  **15.** $\left(\dfrac{583.1}{19.7 - 5(3.6)} - 325.9\right)^6$

# Simplifying in Brief: Summary

Here are some questions that will help you to remember to simplify completely.

I. Are there exponents?

    A. Use any applicable exponent laws.

    B. Use radicals to express any fractional exponents.

    C. Use reciprocals to express any negative exponents.

II. Are there radicals?

    A. Perform any roots possible (reduce *factors* of radicand).

    B. Rationalize denominators (monomial or binomial).

III. Are there fractions?

    A. Use multiplication to change complex fractions.

    B. Reduce fractions by canceling *factors* (not terms).

    C. Get common denominators using LCM for adding or subtracting (be careful of $x - 2$ and $2 - x$ types).

    D. Avoid negative integer denominators by multiplying by $\frac{-1}{-1}$.

IV. Can other operations be performed?

    A. Remove parentheses by multiplying (distribute, FOIL where needed).

    B. Combine like terms.

    C. Have all indicated operations been performed that can be?

**Simplify.**

1. $3x - 7x$

2. $\dfrac{x}{x - 3} + \dfrac{2}{x + 4}$

3. $\dfrac{7x - 3x}{\sqrt{8x}}$

4. $\dfrac{x^2 - \frac{1}{4}}{3x^2 + \frac{3x}{2}}$

5. $\sqrt[3]{\dfrac{x^2 y}{18xy^2}}$

6. $(9x^3 y^2)^{\frac{1}{2}}$

7. $\dfrac{5x - 5}{8xy + 16y} \div \dfrac{x^2 - 1}{2x + 4}$

8. $(7x - 2)(11x + 4)$

9. $5x^{-3}$

10. $\dfrac{4x - 6}{-2}$

11. $\dfrac{(3x^2 y^{-2})^{-1}(4xy^{-3})^2}{x^{-1} y^2}$

12. $\dfrac{15}{\sqrt{7} - \sqrt{3}}$

13. $\dfrac{3}{4 - x} - \dfrac{9}{x - 4}$

14. $\dfrac{6x^3 - 24x}{18x^2 - 9x - 54}$

15. $\dfrac{x^2 - 1}{x^2 + x - 2} \cdot \dfrac{x^2 - 6x + 9}{x^2 - 2x - 3}$

16. $11\sqrt{20} - 5\sqrt{45} + 3\sqrt{500}$

17. $(5x^2 - 3x + 2) - (2x^2 + 8x - 7)$

18. $\sqrt{56}\left(\sqrt{21} - \sqrt{14} + \sqrt{2} - \sqrt{\dfrac{7}{2}}\right)$

## Decision Tree

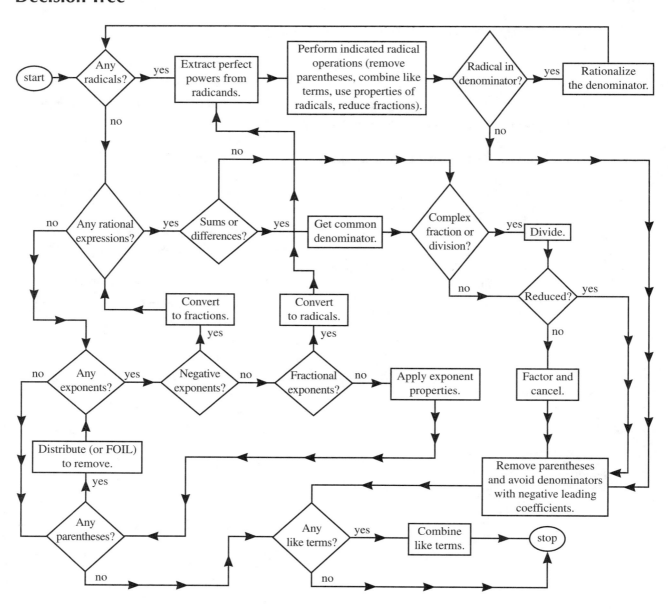

# Variables Applied: Modeling

Sometimes a word problem says that a company could calculate profit using a formula such as $P = -x^2 + 300x + 50$. Did you ever wonder how a company figures out these formulas? Most companies use advanced mathematical methods, but all of these methods are based on pattern recognition. This is also the method used by scientists in determining that $a = -\frac{1}{2}gt^2$ or $D = rt$.

Here is an example for a bicycle company. The production (in bicycles) is 30, 40, 70, 90, and 120 in succeeding years as the company grows. The profit for each year is $900, $1200, $2100, $2700, and $3600 respectively. Now we must ask whether the relation between the production and profit can be expressed by a simple formula. Each profit is 30 times the production, or in other words $P = 30x$.

**1.** Use the formula to predict the profit when 130 bikes are produced. _____

Notice that this conclusion takes some thinking. You may notice that $900 = 30 + 870$, but $P = x + 870$ does not work for the remaining pairs. You may need to consider additions, subtractions, multiplications, divisions, powers, roots, and ratios of these pairs in order to determine the correct formula.

Now see whether you can find the formula for each company and predict the last entry in each chart.

**2.**

| Production | 100 | 120 | 160 | 180 | 200 | lemonades |
|---|---|---|---|---|---|---|
| Profits | 5 | 6 | 8 | 9 | | dollars |

**3.**

| Production | 7 | 8 | 10 | 12 | 13 | sofas |
|---|---|---|---|---|---|---|
| Profits | 343 | 512 | 1000 | 1728 | | dollars |

**4.**

| Production | 20 | 30 | 40 | 50 | 70 | cabinets |
|---|---|---|---|---|---|---|
| Profits | 401 | 901 | 1601 | 2501 | | dollars |

**5.**

| Production | 81 | 121 | 169 | 256 | 270 | bicycles |
|---|---|---|---|---|---|---|
| Profits | 90 | 110 | 130 | 160 | | dollars |

**6.**

| Production | 20 | 30 | 35 | 60 | 110 |
|---|---|---|---|---|---|
| Profits | $\frac{400}{10} = 40$ | $\frac{900}{20} = 45$ | $\frac{1225}{25} = 49$ | $\frac{3600}{50} = 72$ | |

# Rational Expressions in Detail: Explaining Why

What is the sum of $\frac{1}{2} + \frac{1}{3}$? Many Algebra 1 students might answer something like this:

$$\frac{1}{2} + \frac{1}{3} = \left(\frac{1}{2}\right)\frac{3}{3} + \left(\frac{1}{3}\right)\frac{2}{2}$$
$$= \frac{3}{6} + \frac{2}{6}$$
$$= \frac{5}{6}$$

Therefore the sum is $\frac{5}{6}$.

## BASEBALL

How would you answer Baseball Bob if he said that $\frac{1}{2} + \frac{1}{3} = \frac{2}{5}$?

He might go on to say, "I know that $\frac{1}{2} + \frac{1}{3} = \frac{2}{5}$. Here is how I know. If I go to bat twice in the first game of a doubleheader and I get one hit and bat three times in the second game and get one hit, that means that I got two hits in five at bats. That is $\frac{2}{5}$ or .400. Not bad!"

## PIES

That's not all. Baker Bill might say, "I also know that $\frac{1}{2} + \frac{1}{3} = \frac{2}{5}$, and here's how I know."

"Suppose I bake two pies—the same size. I'll cut the first into three equal pieces, and I'll eat one slice. Then I'll cut the second pie into two pieces and eat one slice."

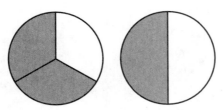

Then he might say, "Obviously I ate two of five slices. But another way of saying 'two of five' is $\frac{2}{5}$. Therefore the sum is $\frac{2}{5}$."

### EVALUATION

You might say, "They did it wrong!" But what did they do wrong, and how do you know they are wrong?

Write a thoughtful paragraph to explain what they did wrong. Your paragraph should include these elements:

- Explain why some might say that $\frac{1}{2} + \frac{1}{3} = \frac{2}{5}$.

- Why would most students disagree with this arithmetic?

- Use a diagram to support your reasoning.

_____

_____

_____

_____

_____

_____

_____

_____

_____

_____

# Practice ······

## SIMPLIFYING RATIONAL EXPRESSIONS

**For what values is the expression undefined?**

_____  1. $\dfrac{x}{x-3}$  _____  4. $\dfrac{1}{x^2+8x-33}$

_____  2. $\dfrac{x^2-1}{x^2-16}$  _____  5. $\dfrac{x^3+x^2+7x+1}{x}$

_____  3. $\dfrac{x-5}{x^3-x^2}$  _____  6. $\dfrac{x^2+4x+4}{15x^2+17x-42}$

**Find the GCF for each pair of polynomials.**

_____  7. $16x^2yz^5$ and $12xy^3z^4$

_____  8. $x^3$ and $x^2-5x$

_____  9. $x^2-9$ and $x^2+6x+9$

_____  10. $2x^2-x-10$ and $2x^2-3x-5$

_____  11. $x^3-4x$ and $3x^3+5x^2-2x$

_____  12. $6x^2-36x-42$ and $4x^2-8x-140$

**Find the LCM for each pair of polynomials.**

_____  13. $16x^2yz^5$ and $12xy^3z^4$

_____  14. $x^3$ and $x^2-5x$

_____  15. $x^2+4x-21$ and $x^2-49$

_____  16. $x^2+6x-16$ and $x-2$

_____  17. $10x^2+21x-10$ and $8x^2+22x+5$

_____  18. $9x^5-90x^4+225x^3$ and $12x^5-60x^4$

**Simplify each rational expression.**

_____ **19.** $\dfrac{14x^3y^2z^4}{10x^2y^5z}$　　_____ **25.** $\dfrac{x^2 - 2x - 24}{x^2 + 9x + 20}$

_____ **20.** $\dfrac{3x - 12}{5x - 20}$　　_____ **26.** $\dfrac{4x - 8y}{8x^2 - 32y^2}$

_____ **21.** $\dfrac{x^2 + 7x - 18}{x^2 + 6x - 27}$　　_____ **27.** $\dfrac{2x^5 + 6x^4}{x^6 - 6x^5}$

_____ **22.** $\dfrac{4x + 12}{2x^2 - 18}$　　_____ **28.** $\dfrac{6x^2 - 13x + 6}{10x^2 - 13x - 3}$

_____ **23.** $\dfrac{6x^2y + 24xy}{15xy^2}$　　_____ **29.** $\dfrac{12x^3 - 90x^2 + 150x}{3x^2 - 15x}$

_____ **24.** $\dfrac{27x + 54y + 81}{6xy + 12y^2 + 18y}$　　_____ **30.** $\dfrac{3x^2 + 39x + 66}{3x^2 + 12x + 12}$

# ■ Practice

## MULTIPLYING & DIVIDING RATIONAL EXPRESSIONS

**Multiply. Leave answers in factored form.**

_____  1. $\frac{3}{5} \cdot \frac{4}{7}$

_____  2. $\frac{15}{17} \cdot \frac{4}{5}$

_____  3. $\frac{32a^3b}{14ab^3} \cdot \frac{7ab^3}{ab^2}$

_____  4. $\frac{25pq}{40q} \cdot \frac{12p^2}{15pq}$

_____  5. $\frac{x+8}{33} \cdot \frac{11}{x+8}$

_____  6. $\frac{x-2}{x} \cdot \frac{x+7}{x-2}$

_____  7. $\frac{x^3y}{(x+4)(x-1)} \cdot \frac{(x-2)(x+4)}{xy(x-2)}$

_____  8. $\frac{(3x+5)(2x-3)}{4x(2x-7)} \cdot \frac{2x^2(2x-7)}{(2x-3)(3x+1)}$

_____  9. $\frac{x^2-9}{x^2-4x} \cdot \frac{x^2-16}{x^2+3x}$

_____ 10. $\frac{x^2+6x+5}{x^2-2x-3} \cdot \frac{x-5}{x^2+2x-15}$

**Divide. Leave answers in factored form.**

_____ 11. $\frac{9}{2} \div \frac{4}{5}$

_____ 12. $\frac{8}{9} \div \frac{12}{27}$

_____ 13. $\frac{93r^2st}{9rs^2} \div \frac{24st^2}{54rs^2}$

_____ 14. $(50xy) \div \frac{35y}{8x}$

_____ 15. $\frac{x-5}{x+6} \div \frac{x-5}{x+2}$

_____ 16. $\frac{2x-7}{3x+9} \div \frac{2x-7}{3x+9}$

_____ 17. $\frac{x(x-6)}{x^2(x-2)} \div \frac{(x-6)(x+1)}{x(x-2)}$

_____ 18. $\frac{(3x-5)(2x+9)}{(2x+9)(2x-3)} \div \frac{(3x-5)(4x+7)}{(3x-8)(3x-5)}$

_____ 19. $\frac{x^2+4x-12}{x^2+2x-3} \div \frac{x^2-7x+10}{x^2-2x-15}$

_____ 20. $\frac{x^2-25}{3x^2+14x-5} \div \frac{2x^2-7x-15}{4x^2+12x+9}$

**Simplify.**

_____ **21.** $\dfrac{57}{20} \cdot \dfrac{4}{19}$

_____ **22.** $\dfrac{17m^3n}{33mr} \cdot \dfrac{22r^2s}{40ms} \cdot \dfrac{28n}{51mn^3}$

_____ **23.** $\dfrac{a^2}{b} \div \dfrac{a}{b^2}$

_____ **24.** $\dfrac{2x - 3}{3x^2 + 3x} \div \dfrac{4x^2 - 9}{9x^3 + 9x^2}$

_____ **25.** $\dfrac{x(5x + 2)(x - 1)}{(x - 1)(3x + 7)} \cdot \dfrac{(3x + 7)(x - 9)}{x^3(x - 9)(x + 6)}$

# ■ Practice

### ADDING & SUBTRACTING RATIONAL EXPRESSIONS

**Add. Leave answers in factored form.**

_____ 1. $\dfrac{7}{14} + \dfrac{3}{14}$

_____ 2. $\dfrac{x + 2}{x - 6} + \dfrac{x - 3}{x - 6}$

_____ 3. $\dfrac{x^2 + 3x - 5}{x^2 + 4x + 4} + \dfrac{2x + 11}{x^2 + 4x + 4}$

_____ 4. $\dfrac{7}{x + 1} + \dfrac{3}{x - 4}$

_____ 5. $\dfrac{8}{x + 4} + \dfrac{3}{4 + x}$

_____ 6. $\dfrac{3}{(x + 5)(x - 3)} + \dfrac{4}{(x + 3)(x - 3)}$

_____ 7. $\dfrac{x}{13x + 26} + \dfrac{4}{13}$

_____ 8. $\dfrac{x - 6}{x^2 + 2x - 15} + \dfrac{4}{x^2 - 3x}$

_____ 9. $\dfrac{x}{x^2 - 3x + 2} + \dfrac{2}{x^2 - 5x + 6}$

_____ 10. $\dfrac{4}{3x^2 + 2x} + \dfrac{6}{x^2 - 3x}$

**Subtract. Leave answers in factored form.**

_____ 11. $\dfrac{6}{5} - \dfrac{8}{5}$

_____ 12. $\dfrac{11 + y}{y} - \dfrac{y + 3}{y}$

_____ 13. $\dfrac{5a^2 - 3ab - b^2}{(a + b)(a - 2b)} - \dfrac{2a^2 - 2ab + 3b^2}{(a + b)(a - 2b)}$

_____ 14. $\dfrac{x}{3x - 5} - \dfrac{2}{5 - 3x}$

_____ 15. $\dfrac{3}{x} - \dfrac{2}{x - 5}$

_____ 16. $\dfrac{x^2}{x^3 - 7} - \dfrac{3}{2x^3 - 14}$

_____ 17. $\dfrac{5x^2 - 8x}{8x^2 - 72} - \dfrac{x^2 + 12}{8x^2 - 72}$

_____ 18. $\dfrac{x}{5} - \dfrac{3}{x + 1}$

_____ 19. $\dfrac{8}{x^2 - 81} - \dfrac{5}{x^2}$

_____ 20. $\dfrac{12}{49x^2 - 36} - \dfrac{4x}{14x^2 - 12x}$

**Simplify.**

_____  **21.** $\dfrac{\frac{x}{2} - 3}{2 - \frac{1}{x}}$

_____  **22.** $\dfrac{1 - \frac{1}{x}}{5}$

_____  **23.** $\dfrac{\frac{7}{3} + \frac{1}{3}}{\frac{11}{9}}$

_____  **24.** $\dfrac{\frac{1}{x+1} + \frac{2}{x}}{3 - \frac{1}{x+1}}$

_____  **25.** $\dfrac{x - 2}{\frac{x}{5} - \frac{2}{5}}$

# ▪ Cumulative Review  ⋯⋯⋯⋯⋯⋯⋯⋯⋯⋯⋯⋯⋯⋯⋯⋯⋯⋯⋯⋯⋯⋯⋯⋯⋯⋯

**For what values of the variable is the fraction undefined?**

_____  **1.** $\frac{4}{7}$　　　　　　　_____  **3.** $\frac{x^2 + 4}{x^2 - 4}$

_____  **2.** $\frac{3}{x - 1}$　　　　　　_____  **4.** $\frac{2}{x^2 + 1}$

**Find the LCM of**

_____  **5.** 7742 and 8526.

_____  **6.** 10 and $x$.

_____  **7.** $200x + 8$ and 20.

_____  **8.** $x^2 + 3x + 2$ and $x^2 - x - 6$.

**Find the equation of the line passing through (1, 2) and**

_____  **9.** having a slope of 7.

_____  **10.** through $(3, 5)$.

**Graph.**

**11.** $x = \sqrt{7}$

**12.** $x < \frac{14}{5}$

**13.** $x \neq 3$

**14.** $7x - 3y = 11$　　　　　　　**15.** $y = -\frac{1}{4}x + 2$

　　　　　　　　　　　　　　　　　　　$2x + y = 3$

**Simplify. Leave answers in factored form.**

_____ **16.** $\dfrac{x^2 + 5x - 6}{2x^2 + 12x}$

_____ **17.** $\dfrac{10 + 3 \cdot 5}{3(6 - 11)}$

_____ **18.** $x^2 - (x + 1)(x + 5)$

_____ **19.** $\dfrac{5x + 10}{2x + 8} \cdot \dfrac{6x - 30}{3x + 6}$

_____ **20.** $(x^2 y^{-3})^4$

_____ **21.** $5^{\frac{1}{3}}$

_____ **22.** $\dfrac{5}{x - 2} + \dfrac{x - 3}{x - 2}$

_____ **23.** $\sqrt{\dfrac{5}{6}}$

_____ **24.** $\dfrac{14}{-6} + \dfrac{1}{-6}$

_____ **25.** $\dfrac{8}{x^2 - 4} - \dfrac{5}{x^2 - 6x + 8}$

_____ **26.** $\sqrt{63}$

_____ **27.** $\dfrac{4}{3 - \sqrt{5}}$

_____ **28.** $\dfrac{x + 2}{x - 1} \div \dfrac{x^2 + x - 2}{x}$

_____ **29.** $\sqrt{3}\left(2\sqrt{3x} - 5\sqrt{x}\right)$

_____ **30.** $5\sqrt{7} + 3\sqrt{7}$

**Solve.**

_____ **31.** $x^2 = 72$

_____ **32.** $\dfrac{1}{2}x + \dfrac{1}{9} = \dfrac{7}{30}$

_____ **33.** $6x^2 - 7x - 5 = 0$

_____ **34.** $\sqrt{6x - 11} = 13$

_____ **35.** $x^2 - 5x + 2 = 0$

_____ **36.** $5 + x(x - 7) = 3x^2 + 9x - 2$

_____ **37.** $x + y = 4$
$2x - 3y = 3$

**38.** If Pat has 27 coins in nickels and quarters totaling $3.95, how many of

each coin are there? _____

**39.** Factor: $6x^2 + 21x - 12$ _____

**40.** Write from memory:
    **a.** Genesis 1:28     **d.** Judges 7:16
    **b.** Genesis 18:28    **e.** Leviticus 6:20
    **c.** Matthew 6:33

    **a.** _____

        _____

        _____

        _____

        _____

    **b.** _____

        _____

        _____

        _____

    **c.** _____

        _____

        _____

    **d.** _____

        _____

        _____

    **e.** _____

        _____

        _____

        _____

# CHAPTER 13
## *Rational Equations*

## Bible: Cardinal and Ordinal Numbers

*Cardinal numbers* are the numbers describing set sizes: one, two, three.

*Ordinal numbers* are the numbers describing the order of objects: first, second, third.

_____ **1.** Which type is used in equations?

_____ **2.** Which kinds of numbers are always used as adjectives?

_____ **3.** Based on the distinction above, how should we classify $\sqrt{7}, \frac{3}{5}, -8, \pi,$ and 0?

**Give the number in each verse below and classify it as cardinal or ordinal.**

_____ **4.** Numbers 7:78

_____ **5.** I Samuel 9:8

_____ **6.** II Kings 12:6

_____ **7.** Nehemiah 10:32

_____ **8.** Isaiah 36:1

_____ **9.** Ezekiel 40:13

_____ **10.** Amos 1:1

_____ **11.** Jonah 3:1

_____ **12.** Acts 20:3

_____ **13.** II Peter 3:3

**Each verse contains the word *five* or *fifth*. Classify it as cardinal or ordinal.**

_____ **14.** Leviticus 19:25

_____ **15.** Leviticus 27:5

_____ **16.** Leviticus 27:27

**Read Revelation 6 and give a verse that illustrates each of the following (or write *impossible*).**

    **17.** four as a cardinal number _____

    **18.** four as an ordinal number _____

    **19.** fourth as a cardinal number _____

    **20.** fourth as an ordinal number _____

Find the words *hundred* and *hundredth* in a concordance. Give a verse to illustrate each combination below (or write *impossible*).

_____  **21.** hundred used as a cardinal number

_____  **22.** hundred used as an ordinal number

_____  **23.** hundredth used as a cardinal number

_____  **24.** hundredth used as an ordinal number

_____  **25.** Review Ezekiel 5:12 as a memory verse. Give the number used and classify it as cardinal or ordinal.

# Math History: Bhaskara

In the first math history worksheet you learned that our "Arabic numerals" are more appropriately called Hindu-Arabic numerals. The ancient Hindus contributed considerably to mathematics. The Sulvasutras, measurement rules derived from rope stretching for measurement, probably originated before 800 B.C. Hence, the phrase "rules of the cord" comes from the meaning of Sulvasutra. Answer the questions about mathematics from India.

1. Aryabhata wrote a landmark Hindu treatise. What was this major work and when did he write it? _____

2. What major work did Brahmagupta write? When?

_____

3. When did Bhaskara live? _____

4. Bhaskara's most important work included Pythagorean triples and an estimate of $\pi$. What was the book? _____

5. Give his best estimate for $\pi$ in both fraction and decimal form.

_____

6. Like other Hindu mathematicians, Bhaskara ignored the distinction between approximate and exact values. How do we know this?

_____

_____

7. His other book included the first study of rational expressions like $\frac{3}{0}$. Give the title. _____

8. Like that of other Hindu mathematicians, his work contains some errors. One of these errors involves his study of the ratios above. What did he say $\frac{3}{0} \cdot 0$ is equal to? What's wrong with this?

_____

_____

Bhaskara's study of numbers sometimes involved large quantities including squaring ten-digit numbers. Patterns of ratios, factors, powers, and roots interested the Hindu mathematicians. These studies highlight the number systems, trigonometry ratios, and number theory results that remain great achievements for Bhaskara and the Hindu mathematicians.

9. A more modern mathematical genius from India is Srinivasa

   Ramanujan. When did he live? _____

10. Ramanujan was the first Indian to be elected to the Royal Society of

    London. In what year did this occur? _____

## *Graphing Calculator Skills* —————————————

### SOLVING RATIONAL EQUATIONS

You can use a graphing calculator to solve and check rational equations. We'll learn on a simple rational equation. This can be a big help as the equations get more complex. Let's try the following equation:

$$\frac{x-7}{7} - \frac{x+2}{3} = 1$$

On this equation you could use a graphing calculator in several ways. One way is to use it like a scientific calculator to check your work. Another way is to actually solve the equation on your calculator. Let's solve it first.

### SOLVING THE EQUATION

Without your calculator, you might solve the equation like this:

$$\frac{x-7}{7} - \frac{x+2}{3} = 1$$
$$21\left(\frac{x-7}{7} - \frac{x+2}{3}\right) = 21(1)$$
$$3(x-7) - 7(x+2) = 21$$
$$3x - 21 - 7x - 14 = 21$$
$$-4x - 35 = 21$$
$$-4x = 56$$
$$x = -14$$

On a graphing calculator, we can solve this equation in other ways too. First we'll use a table, and then we'll use a graph. Before we can use these tools, however, you must program into the calculator what you want to think about.

To use your graphing calculator, think of this equation as two different objects, one on the left side of the equation, and the other on the right. Think of these two sides as values that move and change, as objects that might increase or decrease when the *x*-inputs change. What makes an equation special in mathematics is that both sides of the equation must have the same value for at least some *x*-value. So when are they the same? That is, when is $\frac{x-7}{7} - \frac{x+2}{3}$ equal to one?

Without any calculators, we know that the two sides are the same when $x = -14$. We can show this with a check:

$$\frac{(-14)-7}{7} - \frac{(-14)+2}{3} = \frac{-21}{7} - \frac{-12}{3} = -3 + 4 = 1$$

Therefore our solution above is correct.

To explore this on a graphing calculator, first define the two sides using the $\boxed{\text{y=}}$ key, $y_1 = \frac{x-7}{7} - \frac{x+2}{3}$ and $y_2 = 1$. On your calculator, the variables may look like "X," "Y1," and "Y2." Make sure you use parentheses when you define $y_1$. You might do it like this:

$$Y1 = (x - 7)/7 - (x + 2)/3$$

### SOLVING BY USING TABLES

Now let's solve the equation with a very powerful tool on your graphing calculator: *function tables*.

- First, find the "TABLE" command.
- Find where you can define your table, perhaps under a menu labeled "TABLE SETUP" or "TBLSET."
- Start your table from "0." Use a "1" for your step size.
- View your table. You should see three columns: for $x$, $y_1$, and $y_2$, perhaps like this:

| X | Y1 | Y2 |
|---|----|----|
| 0 | −1.66667 | 1 |
| 1 | −1.85714 | 1 |
| 2 | −2.04762 | 1 |
| 3 | −2.2381 | 1 |
| 4 | −2.42857 | 1 |
| 5 | −2.61905 | 1 |
| 6 | −2.80952 | 1 |
| 7 | −3 | 1 |
| 8 | −3.19048 | 1 |
| 9 | −3.38095 | 1 |
| 10 | −3.57143 | 1 |

- Scroll up and down through the table; your arrow keys will work here. Look for any interesting patterns that you can find; for instance, compare how the two *y*-columns change.

1. What patterns in the number columns do you see?

   _____

2. What pattern in the table suggests that $y_1$ and $y_2$ might eventually be the same?

   _____

3. In the table, scroll until you find a row where the two *y*-values are the same. What is the *x* value at this row? _____

### SOLVING BY USING GRAPHS

Next, let's use another very powerful part of your graphing calculator: *function graphs.*

- Let's use the same two rules in your graphing calculator, $y_1 = \frac{x-7}{7} - \frac{x+2}{3}$ and $y_2 = 1$.
- Set up your graph. You might wish to start with a standard zoom.
- View your graph. You should see something like this:

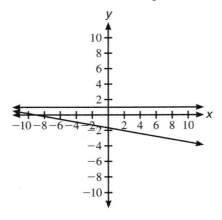

- Study the graphs for any patterns.

**4.** What patterns do you see?

_____

**5.** Where will the two *y*-values be the same?

_____

**6.** Would it help if you changed your window or your zoom? _____

**7.** Finally, find your tracer. Use it to find where these linear functions

intersect.  At what *x* value do the graphs intersect? _____

### CHECKING YOUR SOLUTION

You could solve $\frac{x-7}{7} - \frac{x+2}{3} = 1$ by using either tables or graphs, or you could solve it with pencil and paper. After solving an equation, many students like to check their work. Can you use your graphing calculator to check your work?

Yes, you can! It's very easy. We've already solved the equation twice, and in both cases we found $x = -14$. So you could simply let your calculator evaluate $\frac{(-14)-7}{7} - \frac{(-14)+2}{3}$.

You could do it this way: $((-14) - 7)/7 - ((-14) + 2)/3$. Don't be stingy with parentheses!

**8.** What should you get if *x* truly is $-14$? _____

# Solving in Brief: Summary

A summary for solving equations or inequalities with one or two variables is given below in two forms. Read the outline and notice the types of equations or inequalities and how to solve them. The decision tree gives an analysis of the thought processes used when approaching an equation or inequality. Follow it through to the different conclusions.

I. One Mathematical Sentence

    A. Equations

        1. Linear             —use properties of equality

        2. Absolute Value    —write two equations; connect with *and* or *or*

        3. Rational        —clear fractions

        4. Radical         —isolate radical; square; repeat if necessary

        5. Quadratic      —put in standard form, $ax^2 + bx + c = 0$

           a. Take the root   —if $b = 0$

           b. Factor         —if it factors, set each factor $= 0$ (zero product property)

           c. Quadratic Formula —otherwise $x = \dfrac{-b \pm \sqrt{b^2 - 4ac}}{2a}$

        6. Literal          —use any appropriate method above to solve for given letter

    B. Inequalities

        1. Linear          —use properties of inequality (reverse inequality when necessary)

        2. Rational        —clear fractions (reverse inequality when necessary)

        3. Absolute Value    —write compound sentence: $|y| < 1$ means $-1 < y < 1$

                                              $|y| > 1$ means $y > 1$ or $y < -1$

II. Two Mathematical Sentences

    A. System of equations

        1. Rational          —clear fractions

        2. Substitution Method  —substitute to eliminate a variable

        3. Addition Method    —combine to eliminate a variable

    B. System of inequalities    —graph the solution (see Graphing Review)

**DECISION TREE**

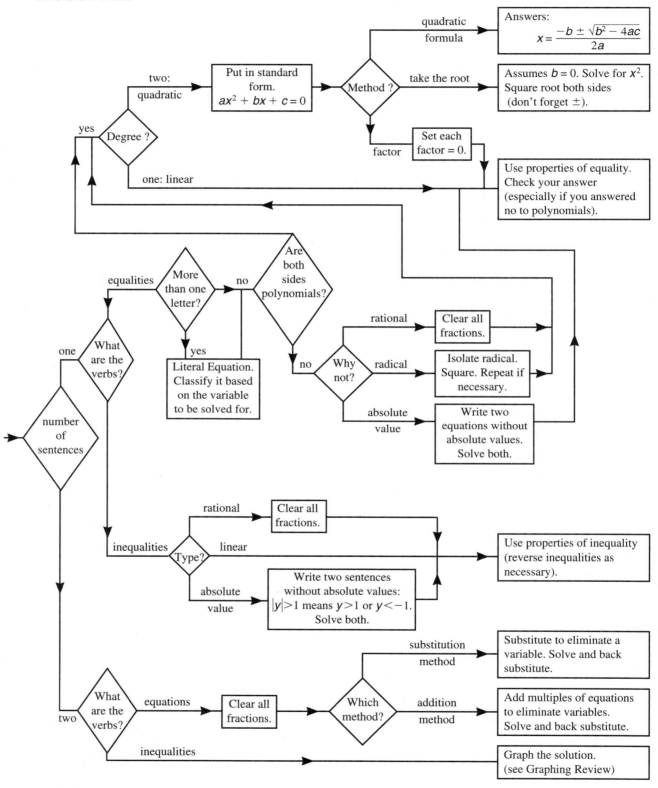

Checking answers is always helpful, but for timed tests it helps to know when the check is an optional self-check and when it is necessary for avoiding extraneous solutions. It is necessary only in

1) Rational equations       —be sure that no denominator is zero
2) Radical equations        —square root cannot be equal to a negative number
3) Absolute value equations —absolute value cannot be equal to a negative number

Remember that some "solve" problems have no solutions: inconsistent systems, quadratics with complex answers, and equations with only extraneous answers. It is also possible to have infinitely many answers as in dependent systems and as in $x = x$.

**Solve for *x* and *y*.**

**1.** $2 - 3x > 5$ _____

**2.** $x^2 + 5x + 4 = 0$ _____

**3.** $xr + 5n = g$ _____

**4.** $\sqrt{x - 5} + 3 = 7$ _____

**5.** $3x - 5y = 7$ _____
$\phantom{5.}\ 2x + 3y = 11$

**6.** $|3 - 5x| < 18$ _____

**7.** $\dfrac{3}{x^2 - 4} + \dfrac{5}{x + 2} = \dfrac{2}{x - 2}$ _____

**8.** $2x + 5 = 1$ _____

**9.** $x + y < 4$
$\phantom{9.}\ x + 3y \geq 9$

**10.** $|x + 3| = 11$ _____

**11.** $x(x - 5) + x^2 - 4 = x^2 - 5(x - 3)$ _____

**12.** $3x - 4x^2 = 1$ _____

**13.** $\dfrac{1}{5}x - \dfrac{2}{35} = \dfrac{5}{14}x + \dfrac{3}{10}$ _____

**14.** $4x + 2y = 4$ _____
$6x + 3y = 6$

**15.** $5x - 3 = 7x + 8$ _____

**16.** $|2x + 8| > 7$ _____

**17.** $2x^2 - x = 5$ _____

**18.** $\sqrt{3x + 7} - x = 1$ _____

**19.** $35 - 2x^2 = 3x$ _____

**20.** $\frac{3}{x} = 9$ _____

# Rational Equations Applied: Electrical Resistance

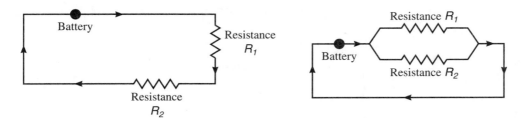

In the first circuit diagram above, the resistors are connected in *series*. Electricity must flow through both resistors. In this case the total resistance $R = R_1 + R_2$.

In contrast, the second circuit diagram shows resistors connected in *parallel*. The electricity current splits, and some flows through one resistance and some through the other. In this case the total resistance $R$ is determined by a rational equation: $\frac{1}{R} = \frac{1}{R_1} + \frac{1}{R_2}$.

Resistances of 7 ohms and 8 ohms are connected in a circuit. Find the total resistance if they are connected in

_____  **1.** series.

_____  **2.** parallel.

An electrician desires to create a total resistance of 10 ohms in a circuit that already contains one resistor. What resistance should he add if the resistors will be connected in

_____  **3.** series, and the first resistor is 6 ohms?

_____  **4.** parallel, and the first resistor is 16 ohms?

Solve the general equation for $R_1$ for a circuit with two resistors in

_____  **5.** series.

_____  **6.** parallel.

_____  **7.** Solve the general equation for parallel resistors for $R$.

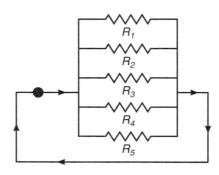

The above diagram shows five resistors in parallel.

**8.** What rational equation relates them to the total resistance?

_____

**9.** If they are 6, 8, 9, 12, and 18 ohms respectively, give the total.

_____

**10.** If the 5 resistances are equal, what resistance should be used to obtain a

total resistance of 20 ohms? _____

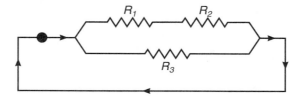

**11.** Give the equation relating the three resistances to the total resistance.

_____

**12.** Find the total resistance if $R_1 = 3$ ohms, $R_2 = 5$ ohms, and $R_3 = 16$ ohms.

_____

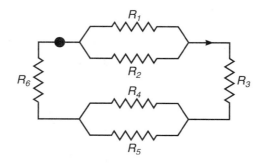

**13.** Give an equation for the total resistance. (*Hint:* consider four objects in
parallel when two of the objects can be found using the idea of question 7).

_____

**14.** If all six resistances are 7 ohms, find the total resistance. _____

# Rational Equations in Detail: Cross-Multiplication

Cross-multiplying is a method for solving equations with a fraction equal to a fraction. For instance, to solve $\frac{x}{5} = \frac{3}{7}$ you can write $7x = 3 \cdot 5$ to get rid of the fractions. Therefore $7x = 15$ and $x = \frac{15}{7}$. The first step is called cross-multiplication and has not been emphasized in this book. Instead, you have learned to find the least common denominator and multiply both sides by that amount. Let's compare the advantages of the method you know with cross-multiplying.

Problem 1: $\frac{x}{3} + \frac{4}{5} = \frac{7}{2}$

1. Clear the fractions and solve as usual. _____

2. Can you solve it by cross-multiplying in the given form? Why?

   _____

3. How could you express the equation to cross-multiply? _____

4. Which method was slower? Why? _____

   _____

Problem 2: $\frac{x}{12} = \frac{7}{6}$

5. What is the LCM? Why can you multiply it on both sides? Solve using

   the LCM. _____

6. What equation do you get by cross-multiplying? Justify it with the multiplication property of equality. Solve for $x$.

   _____

7. After solving the problem both ways, compare your answers. Which was

   more work? Why? _____

   _____

Problem 3: $\frac{x + 4}{x^2 - 9} = \frac{x}{x - 3}$

8. Cross-multiply. What equation do you get? Can you solve it? Explain.

   _____

   _____

9. What is the LCM of the denominators? Use it to clear fractions. What is

   the answer? _____

10. Which method was better? Why? _____

   _____

Which of the problems discussed illustrates each limitation of cross-multiplying?

_____ **11.** It is a recipe, not a principle, and it is easy to forget why it works.

_____ **12.** It is not the shortest method on rational equations having more than two fractions.

_____ **13.** It does not work on many problems with variable denominators.

_____ **14.** It requires more steps for reducing answers.

Conclusion: Cross-multiplication and clearing fractions are identical when the LCM is the product of the denominators and both sides of the equation are single fractions. In other cases clearing fractions will be the better method.

# ■ Practice ·······································································

## RATIONAL EQUATIONS

**Solve each equation.**

_____  1. $\dfrac{p}{11} = -3$

_____  2. $\dfrac{7}{19} = \dfrac{x}{3}$

_____  3. $\dfrac{x-5}{21} = \dfrac{x+4}{15}$

_____  4. $\dfrac{y+1}{3} - 5 = \dfrac{y-2}{9}$

_____  5. $\dfrac{n-3}{12} + \dfrac{n+2}{15} = 2$

_____  6. $\dfrac{k}{16} = \dfrac{k+1}{24}$

_____  7. $\dfrac{2z-3}{70} = \dfrac{5z+1}{42} - 1$

_____  8. $\dfrac{x^2}{3} = \dfrac{5}{4}$

_____  9. $\dfrac{x^2}{18} - \dfrac{3x}{4} = \dfrac{x^2}{12}$

_____  10. $\dfrac{3m^2}{5} - 2 = \dfrac{17m}{15}$

**Solve each rational equation.**

_____  11. $\dfrac{8}{x} = \dfrac{6}{x+2}$

_____  12. $\dfrac{3}{x-5} = \dfrac{7}{x+3}$

_____  13. $\dfrac{12}{2x+4} = \dfrac{3x}{x+2}$

_____  14. $\dfrac{x}{x-1} = \dfrac{4}{x}$

_____  15. $\dfrac{x-2}{3x+4} = \dfrac{2x+1}{x+6}$

_____  16. $\dfrac{3}{x-5} = \dfrac{8}{x-5} + 1$

_____  17. $\dfrac{7}{12x} + \dfrac{3}{8x} = 5$

_____  18. $\dfrac{x+4}{3} - \dfrac{x+2}{4x} = \dfrac{2x-1}{6}$

_____  19. $\dfrac{7}{x-2} + 3 = \dfrac{5}{x-2}$

_____  20. $\dfrac{x-5}{x} + \dfrac{x+1}{x^2-2x} = \dfrac{x-1}{x-2}$

_____ **21.** $\dfrac{1}{9x} + \dfrac{1}{2x^2} = \dfrac{7}{6x^2}$

_____ **22.** $\dfrac{1}{x-4} - \dfrac{9}{x^2+x-20} = 3$

_____ **23.** $\dfrac{x}{x^2+3x+2} = \dfrac{1}{x^2-x-6}$

_____ **24.** $\dfrac{7}{x^2+x-12} + 1 = \dfrac{1}{x-3}$

_____ **25.** $\dfrac{x+2}{x^2-6x+5} = \dfrac{3x}{x^2-2x-15}$

# ■ Practice ..................................................................

### WORD PROBLEMS

1. The sum of the reciprocals of two positive numbers is one sixth. Find the numbers if the second is five more than the first. _____

2. Brad invests $300, some at 6% interest and the rest at 8%. How much should he invest at each rate to earn $20 interest this year?

   _____

3. Susan can clean the house in five hours; Sheila can clean the same house in eight hours; Sarah can clean the house in ten hours. How long would it take them to clean the house working together?

   _____

4. What number must be added to the numerator and denominator of $\frac{4}{7}$ to obtain a fraction equivalent to $\frac{3}{5}$? _____

5. A bicyclist rode 120 miles through the mountains. A car, travelling 4 times faster, drove the same distance in 6 fewer hours. How fast did each travel? _____

6. How much 30% sulfuric acid should be added to seven gallons of 14% sulfuric acid to obtain a solution that is 25% sulfuric acid?

   _____

7. The Conners can paddle across a still lake at 3 mph. When they used their canoeing skills on a river, they found they could go downstream 20 miles in the same time that it takes to return upstream 12 of those miles.

   How fast is the current of the river? _____

8. Two siphons working together can drain an aquarium in twelve minutes. Using only one of the siphons, it takes 30 minutes to drain the aquarium. How long would it take the other siphon to do the job alone?

   _____

9. Kirk has a 10% salt solution. He needs a 3% salt solution for his aquarium. How much pure water and 10% salt solutions must he mix to obtain fifteen gallons of 3% salt solution for his aquarium?

   _____

10. Sam Barton desires to earn $218.55 in interest this year from his three accounts. His accounts earn 5%, 6%, and 9%. He has $\frac{1}{2}$ as much invested at 5% as at 9% and $\frac{2}{3}$ as much at 6% as at 9%. How much is in each account? _____

# ■ Practice

### LITERAL EQUATIONS

**Solve for the given variable.**

_____ **1.** $P = 2W + 2n$ for $W$   _____ **6.** $d = \frac{1}{2}gt^2$ for $g$

_____ **2.** $D = rt$ for $r$   _____ **7.** $\frac{2v}{n} = \frac{r}{k}$ for $n$

_____ **3.** $V = \frac{1}{3}\pi r^2 h$ for $h$   _____ **8.** $\frac{a-b}{2} + \frac{c}{3} = Q$ for $b$

_____ **4.** $A = \frac{1}{2}ap$ for $p$   _____ **9.** $\frac{n}{s} - 3 = \frac{4}{as}$ for $s$

_____ **5.** $A = 2s^2 + 4sn$ for $n$   _____ **10.** $\frac{2p-5}{q} = m^2$ for $p$

**Solve for the given variable. (These require factoring or quadratics.)**

_____ **11.** $B = \frac{1}{7}kq^2$ for $q$

_____ **12.** $\frac{1}{R} + 7 = \frac{3}{Q}$ for $R$

_____ **13.** $M = a^2 + b$ for $a$

_____ **14.** $AB - C = DB$ for $B$

_____ **15.** $a^2 + b^2 = c^2$ for $b$

_____ **16.** $n^2 + 5t^2 = 6tn$ for $n$

_____ **17.** $\frac{xz}{x+y} = 5$ for $x$

_____ **18.** $D = \frac{1}{2}gt^2 + vt + h$ for $t$

_____ **19.** $V = \frac{\sqrt{3}}{12}s^2 h$ for $s$

_____ **20.** $S = 2\pi rh + 2\pi r^2$ for $r$

**Solve for the given variable.**

**21.** $hz - c = 4k$ for $z$ _____

**22.** $C^2 = 9x^2 - PC^2$ for $C$ _____

**23.** $(s-t)^2 = n$ for $s$ _____

**24.** $\frac{ps}{t} = \frac{1}{p} + \frac{p}{t}$ for $p$ _____

**25.** $NG^2 + 3G + Q = AG - F$ for $G$ _____

# Cumulative Review

**Match answers to problems. Answers may be used more than once or not at all.**

_____ **1.** $x - \sqrt{6 - 2x} = 3$

_____ **2.** $x > 8 \wedge x \geq 3$

_____ **3.** $x(x - 5) = -(x + 3)$

_____ **4.** $x > 8 \vee x > 3$

_____ **5.** $|x - 2| < 1$

_____ **6.** $x + y = 4$
$y = x + 2$

_____ **7.** $x^2 = 1$

_____ **8.** $7 - 2x > 1$

_____ **9.** $\dfrac{12x + 60}{2x + 6} \cdot \dfrac{x^2 - 9}{2x^2 + 4x - 30}$

_____ **10.** $2 + \dfrac{1}{x} = 3$

**A.** 1, 3
**B.** (1, 3)
**C.** $x > 3$
**D.** $x \geq 3$
**E.** $x < 3$
**F.** $x \leq 3$
**G.** $1 < x < 3$
**H.** $x < 1$ or $x > 3$
**I.** 1
**J.** 3
**K.** none of the above

**Factor.**

**11.** $-60x^5y^5 + 84x^4y^7 - 8x^2y^2$ _____

**12.** $16x^2 - 36y^2$ _____

**13.** $20x^2 + 60x + 45$ _____

**14.** $x^2 - 5x - 66$ _____

**15.** $15x^2 + 6x - 48$ _____

**Answer each question.**

**16.** Divide $(x^3 - 5x + 7) \div (x - 2)$ _____

**17.** Solve for $v$: $\dfrac{3}{v} + kq = 4n - \dfrac{p}{v}$ _____

**18.** Solve $x - 14 = 3x^2 - 3x - 60$ _____

**19.** Two less than 3 times the reciprocal of a number is the same as the number. Find the number. _____

**20.** If the graph of a line rises from left to right, what is the sign of the slope of the line? _____

**Name each property.**

21. $(3 - x) + 7 = 7 + (3 - x)$ _____

22. $(x - 2)(x + 1) = 0$; therefore $x = 2$ or $x = -1$ _____

23. $-3x < -12$; therefore $x > 4$ _____

24. $\dfrac{1}{x + 2} + \dfrac{2}{x} = 4$; therefore $x + 2(x + 2) = 4x(x + 2)$

_____

25. $\left(x^{-2}\right)^{-3} = x^6$ _____

**Simplify.**

_____  26. $\sqrt[3]{200x^7}$

_____  27. $\dfrac{7}{4 - 3x} + \dfrac{11}{3x - 4}$

_____  28. $\dfrac{1}{\sqrt{56}}$

_____  29. $(x^2 + 3)(2x - 1)$

_____  30. $\dfrac{3 + \frac{2x}{x - 5}}{\frac{3}{x + 3} - \frac{1}{2}}$

**Solve.**

31. $\dfrac{1}{6} + \dfrac{x}{15} = \dfrac{3}{2}$ _____

32. $x^2 - 3 = 0$ _____

33. $\dfrac{1}{x - 2} = \dfrac{x^2 + x - 3}{x^2 - x - 2} + \dfrac{1}{x + 1}$ _____

34. $5 + \sqrt{x - 2} = 8$ _____

35. $x^2 - 3 = 4x$ _____

**Graph.**

36. $5x + y = 3$

**37.** $x > -2$

**38.** $y < \frac{1}{3}x + 4$

**39.** $x + y = 17$
$x - 3y = 5$

**40.** Write from memory:
   **a.** Numbers 23:19     **b.** Judges 16:30     **c.** Luke 15:4
   **d.** II Corinthians 5:21     **e.** Ezekiel 5:12

   **a.** _____

   _____

   _____

   **b.** _____

   _____

   _____

   _____

   **c.** _____

   _____

   _____

**d.** _____

_____

**e.** _____

_____

_____

_____

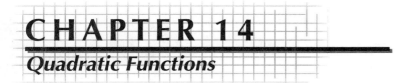

# CHAPTER 14
## *Quadratic Functions*

## Bible: Large Numbers

You have seen that numbers occur frequently throughout the Bible. Perhaps, though, you will be surprised to see how many extremely large numbers are mentioned.

**Investigate numbers of at least a thousand. What multiples of 1000, 10,000, and 100,000 do you find in the verses below?**

_____  **1.** Ezra 8:27

_____  **2.** Nehemiah 7:71

_____  **3.** Esther 3:9

_____  **4.** Matthew 15:38

_____  **5.** Mark 5:13

_____  **6.** Luke 9:14

_____  **7.** Acts 19:19

_____  **8.** Romans 11:4

**The Bible uses many rounded figures but also gives a number of more specific large values. Give the values over 1000 in these passages.**

_____  **9.** Exodus 38:26      _____  **12.** Daniel 12:12

_____  **10.** Numbers 26:7      _____  **13.** I Corinthians 10:8

_____  **11.** Isaiah 37:36

**Find a number at least as large as 1000 in each book below. Give the reference.**

_____ **14.** Genesis     _____ **21.** Song of Solomon

_____ **15.** Leviticus     _____ **22.** Amos

_____ **16.** Deuteronomy     _____ **23.** Jonah

_____ **17.** Joshua     _____ **24.** Micah

_____ **18.** Job     _____ **25.** John

_____ **19.** Psalms     _____ **26.** II Peter

_____ **20.** Ecclesiastes     _____ **27.** Jude

**28.** Give the large number referenced in the memory verse Matthew 14:21.

_____

**29.** How many books of the Bible have you found large numbers in?

_____

# Math History: Apollonius

Apollonius was one of the three greatest mathematicians of ancient Greece (with Archimedes and Euclid, who are discussed in *Geometry for Christian Schools*).

_____ **1.** When did Apollonius live?

_____ **2.** Where was he from?

_____ **3.** Where did he study and teach?

**4.** The Problem of Apollonius appears in his book *Tangencies.* Describe the problem. _____

_____

**5.** His greatest treatise contained eight volumes of material. What was the title of this geometrical study? _____

**6.** Apollonius's work first used the modern term for figures with equations $y = x^2$ as you studied in this chapter. Give his term. _____

**7.** This work also coined the terms *ellipse* and *hyperbola*. Name a mathematician who used Apollonius's ideas to greatly influence modern math.

_____

_____

**8.** Name a modern application of these ideas in astronomy.

_____

**9.** Could Apollonius have made the application of ellipses to astronomy himself? What did he believe about the planets according to his book on astronomy? _____

Apollonius frequently used quadratic equations in his work, much as you used them to graph parabolas. In the work *Cutting-off of a Ratio,* he had to solve a quadratic equation of the form $ax - x^2 = bc$. In the work *Cutting-off of an Area,* he had to solve an equation of the form $ax + x^2 = bc$.

**10.** Apollonius studied geometry and some geometric figures such as lines, circles, rectangles, tangent lines, and solids. Name four additional works that discuss these topics.

_____

_____

# Graphing Calculator Skills: Quadratic Functions

Suppose a younger brother or sister climbed into a nearby tree 20 feet into the air with a ball. A science teacher might tell you that if the ball were dropped, the formula $h(t) = -16t^2 + 20$ would apply. In this formula, $h$ is height in feet, and $t$ is time in seconds since the ball was dropped.

Let's check this on a graphing calculator to see what it means.

### INPUTTING THE FUNCTION RULE

Make sure you input the function rule, $h(t) = -16t^2 + 20$. You'll probably need to think of it as $y = -16x^2 + 20$, with $y$ equal to height and $x$ equal to time.

Put this formula in your graphic calculator. You might need to find a button like "$Y =$" for this. You also may need to write it this way:

$$Y1 = -16 \cdot x^{\wedge}2 + 20$$

### LOOKING AT NUMBER PATTERNS

Next, build a table of values from this function rule. You might press a "TABLE" command, but a good idea would be to set the table up first.

Look for a command like "TBLSET." Here we say where the table should start, and we can decide how much it should skip each time. For instance, if we start with 0 and step by 1 each time, we get this table:

| X | Y1 |
|---|-----|
| 0 | 20 |
| 1 | 4 |
| 2 | −44 |
| 3 | −124 |
| 4 | −236 |
| 5 | −380 |
| 6 | −556 |
| 7 | −764 |
| 8 | −1004 |
| 9 | −1276 |
| 10 | −1580 |

1. Based on this table, when $x = 10$, $y = -1580$. What does this mean about our falling ball? Explain. _____

   _____

2. Would another step size make better sense? Why?

   _____

### GETTING THE BIG PICTURE

Now try a graph of $h(t) = -16t^2 + 20$. Using the "ZOOM" feature is often a good place to start. From here, try a "Zoom Standard." You should get something like this:

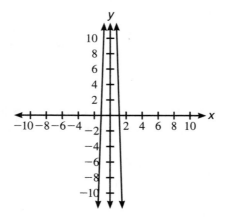

3. What do the numbers on the *x*-axis mean on this graph?

   _____

4. What do the numbers on the *y*-axis mean? _____

5. You could go to a "WINDOW" command to input the smallest and largest *x*- and *y*-values. What window would make good sense for dropping a ball from the tree?

   _____

### EVALUATION

**Now reflect on the following questions. Write a brief sentence to answer each.**

6. What patterns do you see in the graph? _____

7. Does the graph make sense from what you know about falling objects?

   Why? _____

   _____

8. Is there anything about the graph that does not fit with reality? If so, what

   is it? _____

   _____

9. Does the graph suggest that the ball would increase speed as it fell, or

   would it drop at the same rate? _____

   _____

**Now think about the table.**

10. What patterns do you see in the table?

    _____

11. Is there anything about the table that does not fit with reality? If so, what

    is it? _____

    _____

12. Does the table suggest that the ball would increase speed as it fell or
    would it drop at a constant rate?

    _____

13. Finally (and most importantly), is $h(t) = -16t^2 + 20$ an appropriate

    model of a falling ball? _____

# Word Problems in Brief

### SUMMARY

In the Bible worksheet for Chapter 13 you discussed ordinal numbers. Ordinal numbers frequently occur in consecutive number problems.

"Three consecutive numbers sum to 57; find the third number." The word *third* is ordinal. Since you have also studied problems involving fractions, such as one-third, you must be careful to distinguish the fraction context from the order context.

Do you remember how to do each of these?

I. Basic number problems.
   You cannot draw a picture or make a chart. Define your variables in writing and translate literally.
   A. *A number* to be found is described
   B. *Consecutive numbers* are described
   C. *Direct variation. y* varies directly with *x*: $y = kx$

II. Geometry problems.
   Draw a picture. Label variables in the drawing.
   A. *Rectangle perimeter* (such as fence length): $P = 2l + 2w$
   B. *Rectangle area* (such as floor space): $A = lw$
   C. *Triangle angles* (add up to 180°): $\angle 1 + \angle 2 + \angle 3 = 180°$
   D. *Right triangle sides* (Pythagorean Theorem): $a^2 + b^2 = c^2$

III. Chart problems.
   Make a chart using the headings indicated.
   A. *Motion:* $D = r \cdot t$      rate—time—distance
   B. *Substance mixtures*      amount of substance—ingredient percentage—amount of ingredient
   C. *Coin mixtures*      number of coins—unit value (per coin)—total value of coins
   D. *Interest mixtures:* $I = Prt$      principle invested—interest rate (%)—time—total interest
   E. *Work*      time length of job—portion of job completed per unit of time

IV. Optimization problems
   In these problems the answer will be a maximum (largest) or minimum (smallest) value.
   A. One linear condition      —use inequality
   B. One quadratic condition      —find vertex of parabola

## Decision Tree

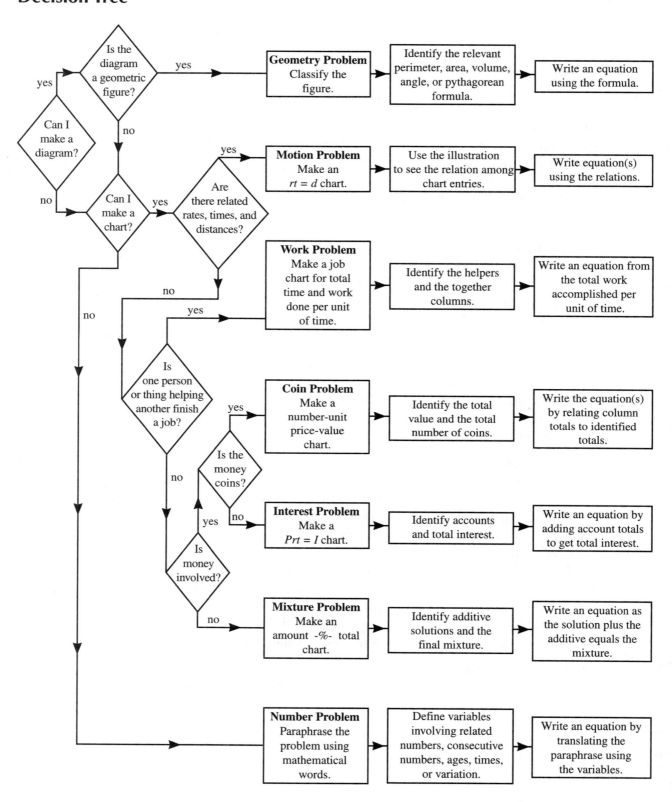

1. The largest angle of a triangle is seven degrees less than five times the measure of the smallest angle. The third angle is fifteen degrees smaller than the largest. Find their measures.

   _____

2. Weed, California, and Sleepy Eye, Minnesota, are 2100 miles apart. Dave leaves Weed at 60 mph, and Fred leaves Sleepy Eye two hours later in his old truck at 50 mph. If each drives non-stop, how long will each

   drive until they meet? _____

3. Twenty less than nine times a number is the same as the product of the

   number and four. Find the number. _____

4. Mary has coins consisting of nickels, dimes, and quarters. She has two more nickels than quarters and five times as many dimes as quarters. If she has $2.50 total, how many of each coin are there?

   _____

5. Terry invested $800 at seven percent interest. How much must he invest at five percent to earn a total of $75 interest this year?

   _____

6. The Porter family used 180 square feet of carpeting in a bedroom. If the length of the room is three feet more than the width, what are the dimen-

   sions of the room? _____

7. Arnold's political experience in Wheeling showed that the number of votes for him varies directly with his campaign publicity expenditures. His nine-thousand-dollar campaign in the last election earned him 6000 votes. To become mayor, he will need 15,000 votes. How much should he budget for his election campaign?

   _____

8. Lisa has two investments totalling $3100, receiving 5% and 8% respectively. If she wants to earn $200 interest this year, how much should she have in each account?

   _____

9. The sum of three consecutive numbers is 75. Find the middle number.

   _____

10. Cindy and Christa work at a flower shop. Christa, being new on the job, takes 30 minutes to prepare six corsages. Cindy can prepare the six corsages in 18 minutes. Working together, how fast could they fill an

    order of six corsages? _____

**11.** The fire department must decide how to save a child at a window twenty feet from the ground. If the ladder is long enough, they won't need to have the child jump into the net. How long must the ladder be if obstructions would force the base of the ladder to be fifteen feet from the

building? _____

**12.** Greg must stain his bacteria culture for a microscope unit in biology. The stain is to be 1.39% violet, but it comes as a 13.9% violet solution. How much purchased stain and pure water should be mixed to obtain 500 ml of the desired stain?

_____

**13.** A canoeist goes six miles upstream against a current of 2 mph and then returns with the current. The total trip takes four hours. Find the rate of

the canoe in still water. _____

**14.** Joe, Pete, and Jerry can rake Mr. Platt's estate in 5 hours working together. Pete remembers a time when he spent ten hours doing it by himself. If Jerry is twice as fast as Joe, how long will it take Jerry by

himself? _____

**15.** Lani has six less than three times as many dolls as Ann. Together they have 70 dolls. How many does each girl have?

_____

**16.** The perimeter of a garden is 86 feet. The length is one foot more than

twice the width. Find the dimensions. _____

**17.** Al's Computer Company finds that when it produces $x$ computers its profits are given by $P(x) = -2x^2 + 800x + 700$. How many computers should they sell to earn the maximum profit? What will this profit be?

_____

# Optimization Graphing Applied

In Chapter 7 you learned how a company can figure out a formula for its profits or costs. You have learned recently how to use the maximum value of a parabola to solve word problems. Each graph below was made by a company with regard to production or financial matters. Identify the optimum value in each graph as directed.

**1.**

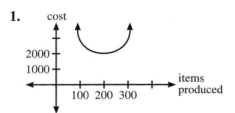

Find the minimum cost. _____

How many items would be produced?

_____

**2.**

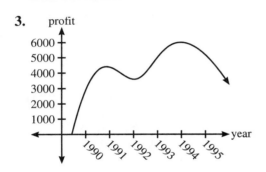

Find the maximum revenue (income). _____

How many items would be produced? _____

**3.**

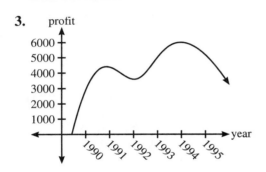

Give the maximum profit. _____

What year did they earn it? _____

**4.**

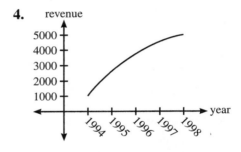

Find the maximum revenue. _____

What year was it earned? _____

**5.**

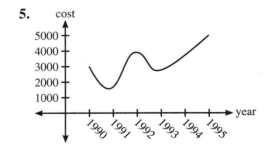

Find the maximum cost. _____

In what year was it spent? _____

**6.**

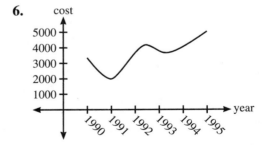

Find the minimum cost. _____

In what year was it spent? _____

**7.**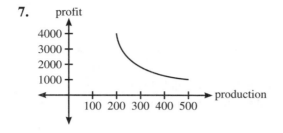

Find the maximum profit. _____

How many items were produced? _____

**8.**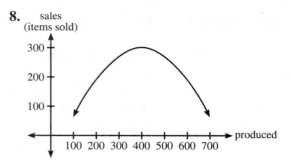

Find the maximum sales. _____

How many items were produced? _____

**9.**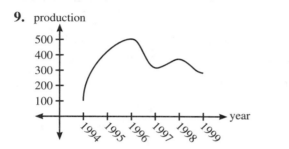

Find the maximum production. _____

In what year was it reached? _____

**10.**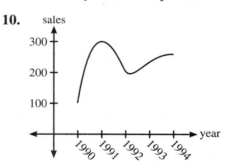

Find the maximum sales. _____

In what year was it reached? _____

# Graphing in Detail

### ZEROS & INEQUALITIES

**Find the zeros of each quadratic function.**

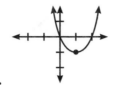

_____  **1.**

_____  **2.** $f(x) = 3 - x^2$

_____  **3.** $f(x) = \frac{1}{4}x^2$

_____  **4.** $f(x) = x^2 - 7x + 12$

_____  **5.** $f(x) = (2x - 7)(8x + 5)$

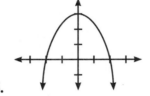

_____  **6.**

_____  **7.** $f(x) = 4x^2 + 8x - 5$

_____  **8.** $f(x) = (x - 3)^2 - 4$

_____  **9.** $f(x) = -\frac{1}{3}x^2 - 7$

_____  **10.** $f(x) = 7(x - 9)^2$

**Graph the inequalities.**

**11.** $\{(x, y)|y \geq x^2\}$               **12.** $\{(x, y)|y > x^2 + 1\}$

**13.** $\{(x, y)|y < -4x^2\}$

**17.** $\{(x, y)|y \geq -5x^2\}$

**14.** $\{(x, y)|y \leq x^2 - x\}$

**18.** $\{(x, y)|y \leq x^2 + 5\}$

**15.** $\{(x, y)|y > 2(x - 3)^2 - 2\}$

**19.** $\{(x, y)|y > x^2 + 5x\}$

**16.** $\{(x, y)|y < 3x^2 - 7\}$

**20.** $\{(x, y)|y \leq (x + 5)^2\}$

# ▪ Practice ·······························································································

## *GRAPHING QUADRATIC FUNCTIONS*

**Find the value of each quadratic function for *x* = −1 and *x* = 2.**

_____  **1.** $f(x) = 3x^2$

_____  **2.** $f(x) = -x^2 + 8$

_____  **3.** $f(x) = x^2 + 7x - 3$

_____  **4.** $f(x) = (x - 2)^2 + 4$

**Give the vertex of each parabola graphed.**

**5.**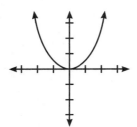

**7.**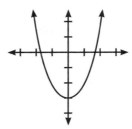

**6.**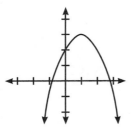

**8.**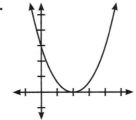

**Put each quadratic equation in standard form.**

_____  **9.** $f(x) = 5 - x^2$

_____  **10.** $f(x) = x^2 + 3x + \dfrac{9}{4}$

_____  **11.** $f(x) = x^2 - 6x + 1$

_____  **12.** $f(x) = 2x^2 + 8x$

**Give the vertex of each parabola.**

_____ **13.** $f(x) = 9x^2 - 7$

_____ **14.** $f(x) = (x - 1)^2 + 4$

_____ **15.** $f(x) = 2(x + 5)^2$

_____ **16.** $f(x) = x^2 + 6x - 8$

**Graph each parabola. Do not make tables of values.**

**17.** $f(x) = 2x^2$

**22.** $f(x) = -3x^2 + 4$

**18.** $f(x) = -x^2$

**23.** $f(x) = (x + 2)^2 + 1$

**19.** $f(x) = \frac{1}{8}x^2$

**24.** $f(x) = -2(x - 1)^2 + 3$

**20.** $f(x) = x^2 + 5$

**25.** $f(x) = x^2 + 8x + 6$

**21.** $f(x) = \frac{1}{2}x^2 - 6$

# ■ Practice ·································································································

## ESTIMATION SKILLS

For each graph below, estimate the value of the function to the nearest 25 or 2.5 as appropriate.

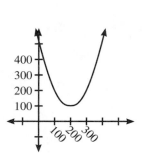

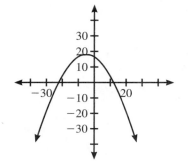

**1.** $f(0)$ _____

**2.** $f(100)$ _____

**3.** $f(200)$ _____

**4.** $f(150)$ _____

**5.** $f(50)$ _____

**6.** $f(-20)$ _____

**7.** $f(-5)$ _____

**8.** $f(0)$ _____

**9.** $f(12)$ _____

**10.** $f(15)$ _____

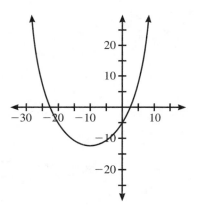

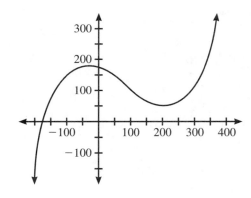

**11.** $f(-25)$ _____

**12.** $f(-10)$ _____

**13.** $f(-5)$ _____

**14.** $f(0)$ _____

**15.** $f(7.5)$ _____

**16.** $f(100)$ _____

**17.** $f(200)$ _____

**18.** $f(0)$ _____

**19.** $f(-100)$ _____

**20.** $f(-200)$ _____

# ■ Practice ·····························································

## WORD PROBLEMS

The height of a projectile after *t* seconds is given by $f(t) = -16t^2 + 160t$.

_____  **1.** How long will it take the projectile to reach maximum height?

_____  **2.** Find the maximum height.

_____  **3.** How long will it take to hit the ground?

The monthly profit of a company that produces *x* units is
$P(x) = -x^2 + 160x - 3700$.

_____  **4.** How many units must be produced for maximum profit?

_____  **5.** What is the maximum profit?

_____  **6.** How many units must be produced just to break even (zero profit)?

Give the dimensions of the largest area that can be enclosed with 84 ft. of fence

_____  **7.** if the area must be rectangular.

_____  **8.** if the rectangle has a river along one length.

_____  **9.** if the area forms a right triangle with a river as the hypotenuse.

_____  **10.** Give the maximum areas in questions 7-9.

# ■ Cumulative Review

_____   **1.** Evaluate $x^3 - 5 + 2x$ if $x = 2$.

_____   **2.** Find $y$ if $x = 3$ where $y = \frac{4}{3}x - 2$.

_____   **3.** Find $f(-2)$ if $f(x) = x^2 + 3x + 1$.

**Give the slope and _y_-intercept.**

**4.** $y = \frac{3}{7}x - 5$ _____

**5.** $2x + 3y + 5 = 0$ _____

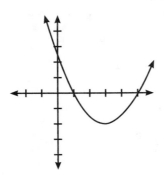

**Refer to the graph for questions 6–8.**

_____   **6.** Find $f(0)$.

_____   **7.** Give the vertex.

_____   **8.** Give the zeros.

**Use the function $f(x) = 2x^2 + 12x - 3$ to answer questions 9 and 10.**

_____   **9.** Does the parabola open up or down?

_____   **10.** Find the vertex.

**Solve.**

11. $x^2 = 6$ _____

12. $5 = 3x + 14$ _____

13. $|x + 7| = 3$ _____

14. $\frac{1}{3}x - 2 = \frac{1}{6}x + \frac{1}{4}$ _____

15. $2 - 5x < 12$ _____

16. $x^2 + 2x - 5 = 0$ _____

17. $\frac{1}{3x} + \frac{2}{x} = 1$ _____

18. $5\sqrt{x + 4} = x + 8$ _____

19. $|3x + 4| > 2$ _____

20. $\frac{1}{2}x \le 5$ and $\frac{2}{3}x \ge 2$ _____

**Simplify.**

_____ 21. $\dfrac{x^2 + 3x + 2}{x^2 - 3x - 10}$

_____ 22. $2(-6) + (-2)(-4)$

_____ 23. $\sqrt{40} - 5\sqrt{10}$

_____ 24. $3^{-2}$

_____ 25. $\dfrac{2\sqrt{3}}{\sqrt{5}}$

_____ 26. $(x + 5)(x + 6)$

_____ 27. $(x^3 - x^2 + 3x - 2) + (x^3 + x^2 - 7x - 1)$

_____ 28. $\dfrac{x^2 - 9}{5x + 15} \cdot \dfrac{5x - 10}{x^2 - 6x + 9}$

_____ 29. $12^{\frac{1}{2}}$

_____ 30. $\dfrac{6x}{-5} + \dfrac{2x}{-5}$

**Graph.**

**31.** $(-5, 2)$

**32.** $\{(1, -1), (-2, 3), (0, 4)\}$

**33.** $x = -3$

**34.** $5y = 2x + 10$

**35.** $y > 3x - 1$

**36.** $y = -x^2 + 2$

**37.** $y = (x + 2)^2 - 3$

**38.** $2y - 4 < x$
$x + 3y < 15$

**39.** A number subtracted from 6 is at least ten. Find the number.

_____

**40.** Write from memory:
   **a.** John 3:16      **d.** Ezekiel 5:12
   **b.** Romans 3:10    **e.** Matthew 14:21
   **c.** Leviticus 6:20

**a.** _____

_____

_____

**b.** _____

_____

**c.** _____

_____

_____

_____

**d.** _____

_____

_____

_____

_____

**e.** _____

_____

_____

# Math History Review

Match the mathematician responsible for the development of each contribution below.
These men are discussed either in the text or the activity manual to *Algebra 1 for Christian Schools*. Each name will be used only once.

_____ **1.** One of the greatest mathematicians ever     A. Al-Khwarizmi

_____ **2.** Irrational numbers as sides of right triangles     B. Nicolaus Copernicus

_____ **3.** Math applied to atomic reactions     C. René Descartes

_____ **4.** Algebra (Arabic)     D. Diophantus

_____ **5.** Contributed to statistics     E. Albert Einstein

_____ **6.** Relativity Theory     F. Bernoulli family

_____ **7.** Algebra (Greek)     G. Carl Gauss

_____ **8.** Calculus     H. Isaac Newton

_____ **9.** Heliocentric Astronomy     I. Pythagoras

_____ **10.** Graphing using coordinates     J. John von Neumann